Grammar-on-the-Go

for Business Communication

Courtland L. Bovée

Professor of Business Communication
C. Allen Paul Distinguished Chair
Grossmont College

John V. Thill

Chief Executive Officer
Communication Specialist of America

Jean Scribner

British Columbia Institute of Technology

PEARSON

Prentice
Hall

Toronto

ISBN-13: 978-0-13-206347-0
ISBN-10: 0-13-206347-6

Acquisitions Editor: Chris Helsby
Signing Editor: Carolin Sweig
Development Editor: Jennifer Murray
Marketing Manager: Toivo Pajo
Production Editor: Richard di Santo
Production Coordinator: Janis Raisen

9 10 11 DPC 11 10 09

PEARSON
Prentice
Hall

Table of Contents

Preface

Demanding course loads mean that not all instructors have time to cover grammar principles in their courses. However, many business students still struggle with English grammar. This new workbook addresses the need of business students to produce clear, correct communication. *Grammar-on-the-Go* can be used in conjunction with your Thill or Bovée business communication textbook or as a stand-alone homework review of the basics of written English. This is a book that keeps its focus on the essential English skills that students—especially those who lack proficiency in business English—need to succeed in today's workplace.

Grammar-on-the-Go opens with a diagnostic test of English skills and an assessment form to let students see where they need to improve. Brief discussions of grammar, mechanics, and usage are followed by Practice Sessions and a three-level series of exercises. Level 1 consists of self-assessment exercises to help students identify specific areas of weakness and overcome them by referring back to the points discussed in the previous sections. Students can find answers to the Level 1 exercises and Practice Sessions in an Answer Key at the end of the book. Level 2 contains real-world exercises incorporating common errors in grammar, punctuation, capitalization, abbreviation, number style, and vocabulary that students learn to recognize and correct. Level 3 consists of a document critique: students correct the errors in the sample business document by using the standard proofreading marks listed in the Correction Symbols list that accompanies the Answer Key.

Listening to instructors and addressing students' needs has resulted in a new, dynamic format for presenting grammar specific to business students. *Grammar-on-the-Go* offers support to business students in a convenient package that can be used either at home or ... on the go!

Grammar-on-the-Go

Grammar and mechanics are nothing more than the way words are combined into sentences. Usage is the way words are used by a network of people—in this case, the community of business people who use English. You'll find it easier to get along in this community if you know the accepted standards of grammar, mechanics, and usage. This supplement offers you valuable opportunities in four sections:

- **Diagnostic Test of English Skills.** Testing your current knowledge of grammar, mechanics, and usage helps you find out where your strengths and weaknesses lie.

- **Assessment of English Skills.** After completing the diagnostic test, use the assessment form to highlight those areas you most need to review.

- **Essentials of Grammar, Mechanics, and Usage with Practice Sessions.** This section helps you quickly review the basics. You can study the things you've probably already learned but may have forgotten about grammar, punctuation, mechanics (including capitalization, abbreviation, number style, and word division), and vocabulary (including frequently confused words, frequently misused words, frequently misspelled words, and transitional words and phrases). Practice sessions throughout this section help you test yourself and reinforce what you learn. Use this essential review not only to study and improve your English skills but also as a reference for any questions you may have during this course.

- **Exercises to Improve Your Grammar, Mechanics, and Usage.** This three-part section helps you to improve your knowledge of and power over English grammar, mechanics, and usage. It includes activities on three levels of difficulty. Level 1, with its self-assessment exercises, helps you identify specific areas of weakness and overcome them by reviewing the basics presented in the Essentials section. The real-world exercises in Level 2 contain common errors in grammar, mechanics, and vocabulary that are found in workplace writing. Level 3 is a document critique, where you are given a document containing errors that you correct using the standard proofreading marks shown in the Correction Symbols list (p. 179).

Without a firm grasp of the basics of grammar, punctuation, mechanics, and vocabulary, you risk being misunderstood, damaging your company's image, losing money for your company, and possibly even losing your job. However, once you develop strong English skills, you will create clear and concise messages, you will enhance your company's image as well as your own, and you will not only increase your company's profits but expand your own chances of success.

Diagnostic Test of English Skills

Use this test to help you determine whether you need more practice with grammar, punctuation, mechanics, or vocabulary. When you've answered all the questions, look at the answer key on page 163 in order to score the test. Then, on the *Assessment of English Skills* form (page 9), record the number of questions you answered correctly in each section.

The following choices apply to items 1–10. In each blank, write the letter of the choice that best describes each sentence.

A.   sentence incomplete

B.   too many phrases/clauses strung together

C.   modifying elements misplaced (dangling)

D.   structure not parallel

E.   nothing wrong

_____ **1.**   Stop here.

_____ **2.**   Your duties are interviewing, hiring, and also to fire employees.

_____ **3.**   After their presentation, I was still undecided.

_____ **4.**   Speaking freely, the stock was considered a bargain.

_____ **5.**   Margaret, pressed for time, turned in unusually sloppy work.

_____ **6.**   Typing and filing, routine office chores.

_____ **7.**   With care, edit the report.

_____ **8.**   When Paul came to work here, he brought some outmoded ideas, now he has accepted our modern methods.

4

_____ **9.**   To plan is better than improvising.

_____ **10.**   Hoping to improve performance, practice is advisable.

The following choices apply to items 11–20. In each blank, write the letter of the choice that identifies the underlined word(s) in each sentence.

A.   subject

B.   verb

C.   object

D.   modifier

E.   conjunction/preposition

_____ **11.**   Take his <u>memo</u> upstairs.

_____ **12.**   Before leaving, he <u>repaired</u> the photocopier.

_____ **13.**   <u>Velnor, Inc.</u>, will soon introduce a new product line.

_____ **14.**   We must hire only <u>qualified</u>, ambitious graduates.

_____ **15.**   They <u>are having</u> trouble with their quality control systems.

_____ **16.**   After she wrote the report, Jill waited eagerly <u>for</u> a response.

_____ **17.**   The route to the plant isn't paved <u>yet</u>.

_____ **18.**   See <u>me</u> after the meeting.

_____ **19.**   Your new <u>home</u> is ready and waiting.

_____ **20.**   BFL is large <u>but</u> caring.

In the blanks for items 21–30, write the letter of the word that best completes each sentence.

_____ **21.** Starbucks (A. is, B. are) opening five new stores in British Columbia in the next year.

_____ **22.** There (A. is, B. are) 50 applicants for the job opening.

_____ **23.** Anyone who wants to be (A. their, B. his or her) own boss should think about owning a franchise.

_____ **24.** Neither of us (A. was, B. were) prepared for the meeting.

_____ **25.** Another characteristic of a small business is that (A. they tend, B. it tends) to be more innovative than larger firms.

_____ **26.** After he had (A. saw, B. seen) the revised budget, Raymond knew he wouldn't be getting a new desk.

_____ **27.** The number of women-owned small businesses (A. has, B. have) increased sharply in the past two decades.

_____ **28.** If I (A. was, B. were) you, I'd stop sending personal e-mails at work.

_____ **29.** Eugene (A. lay, B. laid) the files on the desk.

_____ **30.** Either FedEx or UPS (A. has, B. have) been chosen as our preferred shipping service.

The following choices apply to items 31–40. In each blank, write the letter of the choice that best describes each sentence.

A. all punctuation used correctly

B. some punctuation used incorrectly or incorrectly omitted

6

_____ **31.** The president who rarely gave interviews, agreed to write an article for the company newsletter.

_____ **32.** Give the assignment to Karen Schiff, the new technical writer.

_____ **33.** Could you please send a replacement for Item No. 3-303.

_____ **34.** Debbie said that, "technicians must have technical degrees."

_____ **35.** We'll have branches in Dartmouth, Nova Scotia, Moncton, New Brunswick, and Charlottetown, Prince Edward Island.

_____ **36.** Before leaving her secretary finished typing the memo.

_____ **37.** How many of you consider yourselves "computer literate?"

_____ **38.** This, then, is our goal: to increase market share by 50 percent.

_____ **39.** They plan to move soon, however, they still should be invited.

_____ **40.** Health, wealth, and happiness—those are my personal goals.

The following choices apply to items 41–50. In each blank, write the letter of the choice that best describes each sentence.

A. error in punctuation

B. error in use of abbreviations or symbols

C. error in use of numbers

D. error in capitalization

E. no errors

_____ **41.** Most of last year's sales came from the Queen street store.

_____ **42.** We can provide the items you are looking for @ $2 each.

_____ **43.** Alex noted: "few of our competitors have tried this approach."

_____ **44.** Address the letter to professor Elliott Barker, Psychology Department, Queen's University.

_____ **45.** They've recorded 22 complaints since yesterday, all of them from long-time employees.

_____ **46.** Leslie's presentation—"New Markets for the Nineties," was well organized.

_____ **47.** We're having a sale on childrens' sportswear, beginning Wednesday, August 15.

_____ **48.** About 50 of the newly inducted members will be present.

_____ **49.** Mister Spencer has asked me to find 10 volunteers.

_____ **50.** Let's meet in Beth and Larry's office at one o'clock.

In the blanks for items 51–60, write the letter of the word or expression that best completes each sentence.

_____ **51.** Will having a degree (A. affect, B. effect) my chances for promotion?

_____ **52.** Place the latest drawings (A. beside, B. besides) the others.

_____ **53.** Try not to (A. loose, B. lose) this key; we will charge you a fee to replace it.

_____ **54.** Let us help you choose the right tie to (A. complement, B. compliment) your look.

_____ **55.** The five interviewers should discuss the candidates' qualifications (A. among, B. between) themselves.

_____ **56.** New employees spend their time looking for (A. perspective, B. prospective) clients.

_____ **57.** Amira writes advertising copy (A. as if, B. like) she has been in the business all her life.

_____ **58.** He took those courses to (A. farther, B. further) his career.

_____ **59.** We are (A. anxious, B. eager) to see you next Thursday.

_____ **60.** All commissions will be (A. disbursed, B. dispensed, C. dispersed) on the second Friday of every month.

Assessment of English Skills

In the space provided below, record the number of questions you answered correctly.

Questions	Number You Got Correct	Skill Area
1–10	_____	Sentence structure
11–20	_____	Grammar: Parts of speech
21–30	_____	Grammar: Verbs and agreement
31–40	_____	Punctuation
41–50	_____	Punctuation and mechanics
51–60	_____	Vocabulary

If you scored 8 or lower in any of the skill areas, focus on those areas in the appropriate sections of this supplement.

Essentials of Grammar, Mechanics, and Usage

The sentence below looks innocent, but is it really?

> We sell tuxedos as well as rent.

You might sell rent, but it's highly unlikely. Whatever you're selling, some people will ignore your message because of a blunder like this. The following sentence has a similar problem:

> Vice-President Eldon Neale told his chief engineer that he would no longer be with Avix, Inc., as of June 30.

Is Eldon or the engineer leaving? No matter which side the facts are on, the sentence can be read the other way. Now look at this sentence:

> The year before we budgeted more for advertising sales were up.

Confused? Perhaps this is what you meant:

> The year before, we budgeted more for advertising. Sales were up.

Maybe you meant this:

> The year before we budgeted more for advertising, sales were up.

The meaning of language falls into bundles called sentences. A listener or reader can take only so much meaning before filing a sentence away and getting ready for the next one. So, as a business writer, you have to know what a sentence is. You need to know where one ends and the next one begins.

If you want to know what a sentence is, you have to find out what goes into it, what its ingredients are. Luckily, the basic ingredients of an English sentence are simple: The words you use combine with punctuation, mechanics, and vocabulary to convey meaning.

1.0   Grammar

Grammar is the study of how words come together to form sentences. Depending on their meaning, form, and function, English words fall into various parts of speech: nouns, pronouns, verbs, adjectives, adverbs, prepositions, conjunctions, articles, and interjections. You will communicate more clearly if you understand how each of these parts of speech operates in a sentence.

1.1   Nouns

A noun names a person, place, or thing. Anything you can see or detect with one of your other senses has a noun to name it. Some things you can't see or sense are also nouns—ions, for example, or space. So are things that exist as ideas, such as accuracy and height. (You can see that something is accurate or that a building is tall, but you can't see the idea of accuracy or the idea of height.) These names for ideas are known as abstract nouns. The simplest nouns are the names of things you can see or touch: car, building, cloud, brick.

1.1.1   Proper Nouns and Common Nouns

So far, all the examples of nouns have been common nouns, referring to general classes of things. The word *building* refers to a whole class of structures. Common nouns such as *building* are not capitalized.

If you want to talk about one particular building, however, you might refer to the Glazier Building. The name is capitalized, indicating that *Glazier Building* is a proper noun.

Here are three sets of common and proper nouns for comparison:

Common	Proper
city	Langley City
company	Blaisden Company
store	Books Galore

1.1.2   Nouns as Subject and Object

Nouns may be used in sentences as subjects or objects. That is, the person, place, idea, or thing that is being or doing (subject) is represented by a noun. So is the person, place, idea, or thing that is being acted on (object). In the following sentence, the nouns are underlined.

The <u>secretary</u> keyboarded the <u>report</u>.

The secretary (subject) is acting in a way that affects the report (object). The following sentence is more complicated:

The <u>installer</u> delivered the <u>carpeting</u> to the <u>customer</u>.

Installer is the subject. *Carpeting* is the object of the main part of the sentence (acted on by the installer), while *customer* is the object of the preposition *to* (see Sections 1.2.4 and 1.6.1) in the phrase *to the customer*. Nevertheless, both *carpeting* and *customer* are objects.

1.1.3   Plural Nouns

Nouns can be either singular or plural. The usual way to make a plural noun is to add *s* to the singular form of the word:

Singular	Plural
rock	rocks
picture	pictures
song	songs

Many nouns have other ways of forming the plural. Letters, numbers, and words used as words (as in "Locate the word *their*") are sometimes made plural by adding an apostrophe and an *s*. Very often, *'s* is used with abbreviations that have periods, lower case letters that stand alone, and capital letters that might be confused with words when made into plurals:

Spell out all *St.*'s and *Ave.*'s.

He divided the page with a row of *x*'s.

Sarah will register the *A*'s through the *G*'s at the convention.

In other cases, however, the apostrophe may be left out:

They'll review their ABCs.

The stock market climbed through most of the 1980s.

Circle all *the*s in the paragraph.

In some of these examples, the letters used as letters and words used as words are *italicized* (a mechanics issue that is discussed later).

Other nouns, such as those below, are so-called irregular nouns; they form the plural in some way other than simply adding *s:*

Singular	**Plural**
tax	taxes
specialty	specialties
cargo	cargoes
shelf	shelves
child	children
woman	women
tooth	teeth
mouse	mice
parenthesis	parentheses
son-in-law	sons-in-law
editor-in-chief	editors-in-chief

14

Rather than memorize a lot of rules about forming plurals, use a dictionary. If the dictionary says nothing about the plural of a word, it's formed in the usual way: by adding *s*. If the plural is formed in some irregular way, the dictionary often shows the plural spelling.

1.1.4 Possessive Nouns

A noun becomes possessive when it's used to show the ownership of something. Then you add *'s* to the word:

the man's car   the woman's apartment

However, ownership does not need to be legal:

the secretary's desk   the company's balance sheet

Also, ownership may be nothing more than an automatic association:

a day's work   the job's prestige

An exception to the rule about adding *'s* to make a noun possessive occurs when the word is singular and already has two "s" sounds at the end. In cases like the following, an apostrophe is all that's needed:

the crisis' dimensions   Mr. Moses' application

When the noun has only one "s" sound at the end, however, retain the *'s:*

Chris's book   Carolyn Nuss's office

With hyphenated nouns (compound nouns), add *'s* to the last word:

Hyphenated Noun	Possessive Noun
mother-in-law	mother-in-law's
mayor-elect	mayor-elect's

To form the possessive of plural nouns, just begin by following the same rule as with singular nouns: add *'s*. However, if the plural noun already ends in an *s* (as most do), drop the *s* and add only the apostrophe:

the clients' complaints   employees' benefits

Practice Session: Nouns

Underline the preferred choice within each set of parentheses in the following sentences. Answers to these exercises appear on page 163.

1.   We are moving company headquarters to New York (*City, city*).

2.   The historic Taylor (*Building, building*) is the site of the press conference; the (*Building, building*) is located in downtown Toronto.

3.   During the conference, our staff will be staying at the Hyatt, Fairmont, and Marriott (*Hotels, hotels*).

4.   Accuracy requires that you cross your (*ts, t's*) and dot your (*is, i's*).

5.   The industry has been on a downward spiral since the early (*1990's, 1990s*).

6.   The new (*shelfs, shelves*) will be installed on Friday.

7.   Our (*specialtys, specialties*) are unparalleled service and premium brands.

8.   As a result of several Internet-related (*cases, case's*), the copyright laws are under scrutiny.

9.   Before a job interview, you should learn about the (*company's, companies'*) mission statement.

10.   Sending the newsletter to the printer is the (*editor's-in-chief, editor-in-chief's*) responsibility.

11.   All the downtown (*business', businesses', businesses's*) signs must be repainted.

12. Because the (*passenger's, passengers'*) luggage had been damaged, they had to file claims with the airline.

13. Dealing with angry customers is all in a (*days, day's, days'*) work for Mr. Jemas.

14. Its large airport is one of (*Dallases, Dallas', Dallas's*) main appeals for industrial firms.

15. We were sceptical of (*Jone's, Jones', Jones's*) plan.

Improve Your Grammar, Mechanics, and Usage

Level 1: Self-Assessment—Nouns

Use the following self-assessment exercises to improve your knowledge of and power over English grammar, mechanics, and usage. Answers to Level 1 exercises appear on page 163.

Review all of Section 1.1 and then look at the following 15 items.

In items 1–5, underline the common nouns and circle the proper nouns.

1. Give the balance sheet to Melissa.

2. We'd like to order 50 more cases for Craigmont Stores, and 3 each for the other stores on our list.

3. Tarnower Corporation donates a portion of its profits to charity every year.

4. Which aluminum bolts are packaged?

5. Please send the Joneses a dozen of the following: stopwatches, canteens, headbands, and wristbands.

In items 6–10, underline the subjects and circle the objects.

6. The technician has already repaired the machine for the client.

7. An attorney will talk to the group about incorporation.

8. After her vacation, the buyer prepared a third-quarter budget.

9. The new flat monitors are serving our department very well.

10. Accuracy overrides speed in importance.

In items 11–15, underline inappropriate noun plurals and possessives, and write the correct form in the space provided:

11. _____ Make sure that all copys include the new addresses.

12. _____ Ask Jennings to collect all employee's donations for the United Way drive.

13. _____ Charlie now has two son-in-laws to help him with his two online business's.

14. _____ Avoid using too many parenthesises when writing your reports.

15. _____ Follow President Burgesses rules about what makes up a weeks work.

Level 2: Workplace Applications

The following items may contain errors in grammar, capitalization, punctuation, abbreviation, number style, and vocabulary. Rewrite each sentence in the space provided, correcting all errors. Write *C* in the space after any sentence that is already correct.

1. If a broken down unproductive guy like Carl can get a raise; why can't a take charge guy like me get one?

_____

2. Visit our Web site and sign up for "On Your Toes," our free newsletter that keeps you informed of promotions, discounts and about Internet-only specials.

_____

3.   As of March, 2009, the Board of Directors have 9 members including: three women, one First Nations, and one of East Asian descent.

---

4.   As one of the nearly 275 thousand Maritime Life policyholder eligible to vote, we urge you to approve the new investment advisory agreement.

---

5.   Gerrald Higgins, vice president for marketing, told us reporters that CIBC provides financial services to one-eighth of homes in Canada.

---

6.   Our Customer Relations associates work with people everyday to answer questions, provide assistance, and helping solve problems.

---

7.   If anyone breaches the lease, its likely that the landlord will file legal action against them to collect on the remainder of they're lease.

---

8.   An RESP is one of the most common plans for educational savings because of it's ease of setting up and administering.

---

9.   My advise to you is, to put you're mission statement on your web cite.

---

10. According to Karen Smiths' report small-business owners do'nt recognize the full effect that layoffs and terminations are liable to have on the motivation of surviving employees'.

---

11. To expedite the processing of your Revenue Canada tax return, use the mailing label and bar-coded envelope that comes with your tax package.

---

12. The student association has implemented a exciting array of programs that make it more easy for opinions and concerns to be voiced by you.

---

13. Keep in mind the old saying "When we laugh the world laugh with us, when you cry you cry alone."

---

14. Albert Edmunds and me are Owners of the real estate firm of Edmunds & Cale, which have recently opened a new office in Corner Brook, NL.

---

15. The memo inferred that the economic downturn will have a greater affect on the company's bottom line then we previously assumed, this was the worse news we could of gotten.

Level 3: Document Critique

The following document may contain errors in grammar, capitalization, punctuation, abbreviation, number style, word division, and vocabulary. Correct all errors using standard proofreading marks; refer to the Correction Symbols list.

Memo

TO: All Employees

FROM: R. Smith, Personnel Director

DATE: December 28, 2009

SUBJECT: Time Cards

After reviewing our Current Method of keeping track of employee hours; we have concluded that time cards leave a lot to be desired. So starting Monday, we have a new system, a time clock. You just have to punch in and punch out; whenever you will come and go from your work area's.

The new system may take a little while to get use to, but should be helpful to those of us who are making a new years resolution to be more punctual.

Happy New Year to all!

eg

1.2 Pronouns

A pronoun is a word that stands for a noun; it saves repeating the noun:

> Drivers have some choice of weeks for vacation, but *they* must notify this office of *their* preference by March 1.

The pronouns *they* and *their* stand in for the noun *drivers*. The noun that a pronoun stands for is called the antecedent of the pronoun; *drivers* is the antecedent of *they* and *their*.

When the antecedent is plural, the pronoun that stands in for it has to be plural; *they* and *their* are plural pronouns because *drivers* is plural. Likewise, when the antecedent is singular, the pronoun has to be singular:

> We thought the *contract* had expired, but we soon learned that *it* had not.

1.2.1 Multiple Antecedents

Sometimes a pronoun has a double (or even a triple) antecedent:

> *Kathryn Boettcher* and *Luis Gutierrez* went beyond *their* sales quotas for January.

If taken alone, *Kathryn Boettcher* is a singular antecedent. So is *Luis Gutierrez*. However, when together they are the plural antecedent of a pronoun, so the pronoun has to be plural. Thus the pronoun is *their* instead of *her* or *his*.

1.2.2 Unclear Antecedents

In some sentences the pronoun's antecedent is unclear:

> Sandy Wright sent Jane Brougham *her* production figures for the previous year. *She* thought they were too low.

To which person does the pronoun *her* refer? Someone who knew Sandy and Jane and knew their business relationship might be able to figure out the antecedent for *her*. Even with such an advantage, however, a reader might receive the wrong meaning. Also, it would be nearly impossible for any reader to know which name is the antecedent of *she*.

The best way to clarify an ambiguous pronoun is usually to rewrite the sentence, repeating nouns when needed for clarity:

> Sandy Wright sent her production figures for the previous year to Jane Brougham. *Jane* thought they were too low.

The noun needs to be repeated only when the antecedent is unclear.

1.2.3 Gender-Neutral Pronouns

The pronouns that stand for males are *he, his,* and *him.* The pronouns that stand for females are *she, hers,* and *her.* However, you'll often be faced with the problem of choosing a pronoun for a noun that refers to both females and males:

> Each manager must make up (his, her, his or her, its, their) own mind about stocking this item and about the quantity that (he, she, he or she, it, they) can sell.

This sentence calls for a pronoun that's neither masculine nor feminine. The issue of gender-neutral pronouns responds to efforts to treat females and males evenhandedly. Here are some possible ways to deal with this issue:

> Each manager must make up *his* . . .

> (Not all managers are men.)

> Each manager must make up *her* . . .

> (Not all managers are women.)

> Each manager must make up *his* or *her* . . .

> (This solution is acceptable but becomes awkward when repeated more than once or twice in a document.)

> Each manager must make up *her* . . . Every manager will receive *his* . . . A manager may send *her* . . .

(A manager's gender does not alternate like a windshield wiper!)

Each manager must make up *their* . . .

(The pronoun can't be plural when the antecedent is singular.)

Each manager must make up *its* . . .

(*It* never refers to people.)

The best solution is to make the noun plural or to revise the passage altogether:

Managers must make up *their* minds . . .

Each manager must decide whether . . .

Be careful not to change the original meaning.

1.2.4 Case of Pronouns

The case of a pronoun tells whether the pronoun is acting or acted upon:

She sells an average of five packages each week.

In this sentence, *she* is doing the selling. Because *she* is acting, *she* is said to be in the nominative case. Now consider what happens when the pronoun is acted upon:

After six months, Ms. Browning promoted *her*.

In this sentence, the pronoun *her* is acted upon. The pronoun *her* is thus said to be in the objective case.

Contrast the nominative and objective pronouns in this list:

Nominative	Objective
I	me
we	us

he	him
she	her
they	them
who	whom
whoever	whomever

Objective pronouns may be used as either the object of a verb (such as *promoted*) or the object of a preposition (such as *with*):

Rob worked with *them* until the order was filled.

In this example, *them* is the object of the preposition *with*. Here's a sentence with three pronouns, the first one nominative, the second the object of a verb, and the third the object of a preposition:

He paid *us* as soon as the cheque came from *them*.

He is nominative; *us* is objective because it's the object of the verb *paid; them* is objective because it's the object of the preposition *from*.

Note that in formal writing and speech, nominative pronouns follow the various forms of the verb *to be:*

The team leader on the Magna project will be *she*.

Every writer sometimes wonders whether to use *who* or *whom:*

(Who, Whom) will you hire?

Because this sentence is a question, it's difficult to see that *whom* is the object of the verb *hire*. You can figure out which pronoun to use if you rearrange the question and temporarily try *she* and *her* in place of *who* and *whom:* "Will you hire *she*?" or "Will you hire *her*?" *Her* and *whom* are both objective, so the correct choice is "*Whom* will you hire?" Here's a different example:

(Who, Whom) logged so much travel time?

Turning the question into a statement, you get:

He logged so much travel time.

Therefore, the correct statement is:

Who logged so much travel time?

1.2.5 Possessive Pronouns

Possessive pronouns work like possessive nouns: They show ownership or automatic association.

her job   their preferences

his account   its equipment

However, possessive pronouns are different from possessive nouns in the way they are written. That is, possessive pronouns never have an apostrophe.

Possessive Noun	Possessive Pronoun
the woman's estate	her estate
Roger Franklin's plans	his plans
the shareholders' feelings	their feelings
the vacuum cleaner's attachments	its attachments

The word *its* is the possessive of *it*. Like all other possessive pronouns, *its* has no apostrophe. Some people confuse *its* with *it's,* the contraction of *it is* and *it has*. Contractions are discussed later.

26

Practice Session: Pronouns

Underline the preferred choice within each set of parentheses in the following sentences. Answers to these exercises appear on page 164.

1. Just between you and (*I, me*), I don't think we will make the deadline.

2. The final speaker at the luncheon was (*she, her*).

3. When you are finished, give the report to (*he, him*).

4. (*We, Us*) telemarketers have a tarnished reputation.

5. The company is sending the marketing communications staff—Mary-Ann, Alan, and (*I, me, myself*)—to the conference.

6. The company will issue (*their, its*) annual report next month.

7. Anyone who hasn't yet turned in (*their, his or her*) questionnaire should do so by tomorrow.

8. (*Who, Whom*) shall I say called?

9. To (*who, whom*) should I address the letter?

10. (*Who, Whom*) will they hire?

11. We need more people in our department like (*she, her*).

12. When dealing with an angry customer, try to calm (*him, him or her, them*) down.

13. It was either Sarah or Charlene who left (*her, their*) briefcase on the train.

14. The company needs to update (*its, it's*) Web site.

15. (*Who, Whom*) do you think will be given the promotion?

16. Be sure to include (*your, you're*) e-mail address on the form.

17. Each brand should have (*its, their*) own trademark.

18. The "dynamic duo"—Bruce and (*I, me*)—are in charge of next week's office party.

19. The supervisor thanked the team members for (*their, they're*) support.

20. The pharmaceutical giant agreed to take (*their, its*) diet drug off the market.

Improve Your Grammar, Mechanics, and Usage

Level 1: Self-Assessment—Pronouns

Review Section 1.2 and then look at the following 15 items. Answers to Level 1 exercises appear on page 164.

In items 1–5, replace the underlined nouns with the correct pronouns:

1. _____ To which retailer will you send your merchandise?

2. _____ Have you given John and Nancy a list of parts?

3. _____ The main office sent the invoice to Mr. and Mrs. Litvak on December 5.

4. _____ The company settled the company's accounts before the end of the year.

5. _____ Which person's umbrella is this?

In items 6–15, write the correct pronouns in the spaces provided:

6. The sales staff is preparing guidelines for _____ (*their, its*) clients.

7. Few of the sales representatives turn in _____ (*their, its*) reports on time.

8. The board of directors has chosen _____ (*their, its*) officers.

9. Donna and Eileen have told _____ (*her, their*) clients about the new program.

10. Each manager plans to expand _____ (*her, their, his or her*) sphere of control next year.

11. Has everyone supplied _____ (*his, their, his or her*) social insurance number?

12. After giving every employee _____ (*his, their, a*) raise, George told _____ (*them, they, all*) about the increased workload.

13. Bob and Tim have opposite ideas about how to achieve company goals. _____ (*Who, Whom*) do you think will win the debate?

14. City Securities has just announced _____ (*who, whom*) it will hire as CEO.

15. Either of the new products would easily find _____ (*their, its*) place in the marketplace.

Level 2: Workplace Applications

The following items may contain errors in grammar, capitalization, punctuation, abbreviation, number style, and vocabulary. Rewrite each sentence, correcting all errors. Write *C* in the space after any sentence that is already correct.

1. Anita Doig from Data Providers will outline their data interpretations as it relates to industry trends, additionally Miss Doig will be asked to comment on how their data should be utilized.

2. You're order for 2000 mylar bags has been received by us; please be advised that orders of less than 5000 bags only get a 20 percent discount.

3. Just between you and I, the new customer centric philosophy seems pretty confusing.

4. Whether dealing with a catastrophe, or with the many problems that affect a great city on a daily basis; Mayor Taylor has relied on a systematic methodical approach that can work for any manager, in any sized business.

5. Among the specialties of Product Marketers International is promotional efforts for clients, including presence on the Internet, radio, and on television.

6.   An overview of a typical marketing plan will be covered in the introduction to this report, to give you an idea of what's in it.

7.   Franchise sales can be a discreet source of income and compliment your overall sales.

8.   Special events ranging from author breakfasts and luncheons to awards programs and reception's offers a great way to make industry contacts.

9.   We will show you how not only to meet the challenges of information rich material but also the challenges of electronic distance learning.

10.   To site just one problem, the reason that the market is in such a state of confusion is the lack of standards whether for hardware, software or for metadata.

11.   Two leading business consultants Doug Smith and Carla McNeil will share their insights on how specialty stores can effectively compete in a world of Corporate Superstores.

12.   One of the big questions we need to address are "How does buying effect inventory levels"?

13.   The closing of many industry digital entities have greatly affected the perception of e-books as a viable platform.

14.   A competent, motivated, and enthusiastic staff can be a managers' most important asset in a competitive marketplace.

15.   Come by the Technology Lounge where you can log on to computers and plug into laptops and check out demos of sponsor's Web sites.

Level 3: Document Critique

The following document may contain errors in grammar, capitalization, punctuation, abbreviation, number style, and vocabulary. Correct all errors using standard proofreading marks (see the Correction Symbols list on p. 179).

Date: Thurs, 12 November 2009 11:07:33–0800

From: rick glissmeyer < rickg@aol.com>

To: richard herman < rcherman@ddc.com>

CC:

BCC:

Attached:

Subject: Please supply shipping costs

Dear Richard:

As you requested heres the complete order for seed mixes required by Roberta Mcdonald in Vancouver:

* Thirty two kilograms 80/20 canary seed mix @ $7.99

* 30 kg soak seed @ $9.50

* Total order: $540.68

The seeds are to be shipped to:

Roberta C. McDonald

1725 w. Third Av.

Vancuover, BC, V5M-5R6

We will mail our cheque, as soon as you reply with the amount of shipping costs. Roberta says "her flock's getting ready for breeding," and she needs the soak seed by the end of this month.

Thanks for your Quick Srevice

Rick Glissmeyer

1.3 Verbs

A verb describes an action:

> They all *quit* in disgust.

It may also describe a state of being:

> Working conditions *were* substandard.

The English language is full of action verbs. Here are a few you'll often run across in the business world:

verify	perform	fulfill
hire	succeed	send
leave	improve	receive
accept	develop	pay

You could undoubtedly list many more.

The most common verb describing a state of being instead of an action is *to be* and all its forms:

> I *am, was,* or *will be;* you *are, were,* or *will be*

Other verbs also describe a state of being:

> It *seemed* a good plan at the time.

> She *sounds* impressive at a meeting.

These verbs link what comes before them in the sentence with what comes after; no action is involved. (See Section 1.7.5 for a fuller discussion of linking verbs.)

1.3.1 Verb Tenses

English has three simple verb tenses: present, past, and future.

Present: Our branches in Whitehorse *stock* other items.

Past: We *stocked* Purquil pens for a short time.

Future: Rotex Tire Stores *will stock* your line of tires when you begin a program of effective national advertising.

With most verbs (the regular ones), the past tense ends in *ed,* and the future tense always has *will* or *shall* in front of it. But the present tense is more complex, depending on the subject:

	First Person	**Second Person**	**Third Person**
Singular	I stock	you stock	he/she/it stocks
Plural	we stock	you stock	they stock

The basic form, *stock,* takes an additional *s* when *he, she,* or *it* precedes it. (See section 1.3.4 for more on subject-verb agreement.)

In addition to the three simple tenses, there are three perfect tenses using forms of the helping verb *have.* The present perfect tense uses the past participle (which for regular verbs is the same as the past tense) of the main verb, *stocked,* and adds the present-tense *have* or *has* to the front of it:

(I, we, you, they) *have stocked.*

(He, she, it) *has stocked.*

The past perfect tense uses the past participle of the main verb, *stocked,* and adds the past-tense *had* to the front of it:

> (I, you, he, she, it, we, they) *had stocked.*

The future perfect tense also uses the past participle of the main verb, *stocked,* but adds the future-tense *will have:*

> (I, you, he, she, it, we, they) *will have stocked.*

Keep verbs in the same tense when the actions occur at the same time:

> When the payroll cheques *came* in, everyone *showed* up for work.

> We *have found* that everyone *has pitched* in to help.

When the actions occur at different times, you may change tense accordingly:

> The shipment *came* last Wednesday, so if another one *comes* in today, please *return* it.

> The new employee *had been* ill at ease, but now she *has become* a full-fledged member of the team.

1.3.2 Irregular Verbs

Many verbs don't follow in every detail the patterns already described. The most irregular of these verbs is *to be:*

Tense	Singular	Plural
Present:	I *am*	we *are*
	you *are*	you *are*
	he, she, it *is*	they *are*

Past:	I *was*	we *were*
	you *were*	you *were*
	he, she, it *was*	they *were*

The future tense of *to be* is formed in the same way that the future tense of a regular verb is formed.

The perfect tenses of *to be* are also formed as they would be for a regular verb, except that the past participle is a special form, *been,* instead of just the past tense:

Present perfect: you have been

Past perfect: you had been

Future perfect: you will have been

Here's a sampling of other irregular verbs:

Present	Past	Past Participle
begin	began	begun
shrink	shrank	shrunk
know	knew	known
rise	rose	risen
become	became	become
go	went	gone
do	did	done

Dictionaries list the various forms of other irregular verbs.

1.3.3 Transitive and Intransitive Verbs

Many people are confused by three particular sets of verbs:

    lie/lay   sit/set   rise/raise

Using these verbs correctly is much easier when you learn the difference between transitive and intransitive verbs.

Transitive verbs act upon an object; they "transfer" their action to the object. Intransitive verbs do not. Here are some sample uses of transitive and intransitive verbs:

Intransitive	**Transitive**
We should include in our new offices a place to *lie* down for a nap.	The workers will be here on Monday to *lay* new carpeting.
Even the way an interviewee *sits* is important.	That crate is full of stemware, so *set* it down carefully.
Salaries at Compu-Link, Inc., *rise* swiftly.	They *raise* their level of production every year.

The workers *lay* carpeting, you *set* down the crate, they *raise* production; each action is transferred to something. In the intransitive sentences, one *lies* down, an interviewee *sits,* and salaries *rise* without (at least grammatically) affecting anything else. Intransitive sentences are complete with only a subject and a verb; transitive sentences are not complete unless they also include an object, or something to transfer the action to.

Tenses are a confusing element of the *lie/lay* problem:

Present	Past	Past Participle
I lie	I lay	I have lain
I lay (something down)	I laid (something down)	I have laid (something down)

The past tense of *lie* and the present tense of *lay* look and sound alike, even though they're different verbs.

1.3.4 Subject-Verb Agreement

Whether regular or irregular, every verb must agree with its subject, both in person (first, second, or third) and in number (single or plural).

In a simple sentence, making a verb agree with its subject is a straightforward task:

	First Person	Second Person	Third Person
Singular	I *am;* I *write*	you *are;* you *write*	he/she/it *is;* he/she/it *writes*
Plural	we *are;* we *write*	you *are;* you *write*	they *are;* they *write*

David Lee *is* a strong competitor. (third-person singular)

We *write* to you every month. (first-person plural)

Confusion sometimes arises when sentences are a bit more complicated. For example, be sure to avoid agreement problems when words come between the subject and verb. In the following examples, the verb appears in italics, and its subject is underlined:

The <u>analysis</u> of existing documents *takes* a full week.

Even though *documents* is a plural, the verb is in the singular form. That's because the subject of the sentence is *analysis,* a singular noun. The phrase *of existing documents* can be disregarded. Here is another example:

The <u>answers</u> for this exercise *are* in the study guide.

Take away the phrase *for this exercise* and you are left with the plural subject *answers.* Therefore, the verb takes the plural form.

Verb agreement is also complicated when the subject is not a specific noun or pronoun and when the subject may be considered either singular or plural. In such cases, you have to analyze the surrounding sentence to determine which verb form to use.

The <u>staff</u> *is* quartered in the warehouse.

The <u>staff</u> *are* at their desks in the warehouse.

The <u>computers</u> and the <u>staff</u> *are* in the warehouse.

Neither the staff nor the <u>computers</u> *are* in the warehouse.

<u>Every</u> computer *is* in the warehouse.

<u>Each</u> of the computers *is* in the warehouse.

Did you notice that words such as *every* use the singular verb form? In addition, when an *either/or* or a *neither/nor* phrase combines singular and plural nouns, the verb takes the form that matches the noun closest to it.

In the business world, some subjects require extra attention. Company names, for example, are considered singular and therefore take a singular verb in most cases—even if they contain plural words:

<u>Yong Brothers</u> *offers* convenient grocery shopping.

In addition, quantities are sometimes considered singular and sometimes plural. If a quantity refers to a total amount, it takes a singular verb; if a quantity refers to individual, countable units, it takes a plural verb:

> Three <u>hours</u> *is* a long time.

> The eight <u>dollars</u> we collected for the fund *are* stacked on the desk.

Fractions may also be singular or plural, depending on the noun that accompanies them:

> One-third of the <u>warehouse</u> *is* devoted to this product line.

> One-third of the <u>products</u> *are* defective.

For a related discussion, see Section 1.7.2, "Longer Sentences," later in this grammar supplement.

1.3.5 Voice of Verbs

Verbs have two voices, active and passive. When the subject performs the action of the verb, the voice is active. When the subject receives the action of the verb, the voice is passive:

Active: The buyer paid a large amount.

Passive: A large amount was paid by the buyer.

The passive voice uses a form of the verb *to be,* which adds words to a sentence. In the example, the passive-voice sentence uses eight words, whereas the active-voice sentence uses only six to say the same thing. The words *was* and *by* are unnecessary to convey the meaning of the sentence. In fact, extra words usually clog meaning. So be sure to opt for the active voice when you have a choice.

At times, however, you have no choice:

> Several items *have been taken,* but so far we don't know who took them.

The passive voice becomes necessary when you don't know (or don't want to say) who performed the action; the active voice is bolder and more direct.

1.3.6 Mood of Verbs

You have three moods to choose from, depending on your intentions. Most of the time you use the indicative mood to make a statement or to ask a question:

The secretary *mailed* a letter to each supplier.

Did the secretary *mail* a letter to each supplier?

When you wish to command or request, use the imperative mood:

Please *mail* a letter to each supplier.

Sometimes, especially in business, a courteous request is stated like a question; in that case, however, no question mark is required:

Would you *mail* a letter to each supplier.

The subjunctive mood, most often used in formal writing or in presenting bad news, expresses a possibility or a recommendation. The subjunctive is usually signalled by a word such as *if* or *that*. In these examples, the subjunctive mood uses special verb forms:

If the secretary *were to mail* a letter to each supplier, we might save some money.

I suggested that the secretary *mail* a letter to each supplier.

Although the subjunctive mood is not used as often as it once was, it's still found in such expressions as *Come what may* and *If I were you*. In general, it is used to convey an idea that is contrary to fact: If iron *were* lighter than air.

Practice Session: Verbs

Underline the preferred choice within each set of parentheses in the following sentences. Answers to these exercises appear on page 165.

1.   When Hastings (*come, comes, came*) in, tell him I (*want, wanted*) to see him.

2.   Even though Sheila (*knowed, knew*) the right password, she typed it incorrectly.

3.   The presentation had not yet (*began, begun*) when Charles arrived.

4.   What I always say is, let sleeping dogs (*lay, lie*).

5.   The workers (*lay, laid*) the tile in the executive bathroom yesterday.

6.   This is where the president of the board (*sits, sets*) during meetings.

7.   Just (*sit, set*) the boxes down over there.

8.   Do you think management will (*raise, rise*) prices across the board next week?

9.   A list of promotions (*was, were*) posted on the company intranet.

10.   The supervisor of the assembly-line workers (*is, are*) being replaced.

11.   The committee (*is, are*) considering the proposal today.

12.   The board and the committee (*is, are*) having a joint meeting on June 25.

13.   Neither the board nor the committee (*is, are*) expected to approve the proposal.

14.   Every member of the board (*is, are*) going to make a statement.

15.   Katten and Associates (*represent, represents*) clients in the entertainment industry.

16.   Five hours (*is, are*) all I can give you to get the project done.

17.   Half of the vacant lots (*is, are*) already sold.

18. Half of the hall (*is, are*) reserved for the luncheon.

19. Mario suggested that the public relations department (*send, sends*) out a news release about the merger.

20. If I (*was, were*) CEO, I'd fire the whole accounting staff.

Improve Your Grammar, Mechanics, and Usage

Level 1: Self-Assessment—Verbs

Review all of Section 1.3 and then complete the following 15 items. Answers to Level 1 exercises appear on page 165.

In items 1–5, provide the verb form called for in the following exercises:

1. I _____ (present perfect, *become*) the resident expert on repairing the copy machine.

2. She _____ (past, *know*) how to conduct an audit when she came to work for us.

3. Before Joan was promoted, she already _____ (past perfect, *choose*) her new office furniture.

4. Next week, call John to tell him what you _____ (future, *do*) to help him set up the seminar.

5. By the time you finish the analysis, he _____ (future perfect, *return*) from his vacation.

For items 6–10, rewrite the sentences so that they use active voice instead of passive:

6. The report will be written by Leslie Cartwright.

42

7. The transaction was not recorded by me.

_____

8. Have you been notified by the claims department of your rights?

_____

9. Their services are used by our firm for hardware upgrades.

_____

10. The damaged equipment was returned by the customer before we even located a repair facility.

_____

In items 11–15, circle the correct verb form provided in parentheses:

11. Everyone upstairs (_receive/receives_) mail before we do.

12. Neither the main office nor the branches (_is/are_) blameless.

13. C&B Sales (_is/are_) listed in the directory.

14. When measuring shelves, 10 cm (_is/are_) significant.

15. About 90 percent of the employees (_plan/plans_) to come to the company picnic.

Level 2: Workplace Applications

The following items may contain errors in grammar, capitalization, punctuation, abbreviation, number style, and vocabulary. Rewrite each sentence in the space provided, correcting all errors. Write _C_ in the space after any sentence that is already correct.

1. Cut 5 cm off trunk and place in a water stand, and fill with water.

---

2. The newly-elected officers of the Board are: John Rogers, president, Robin Doig, vice-president, and Mary Sturhann, secretary.

---

3. Employees were stunned when they are notified that the trainee got promoted to Manager only after her 4th week with the company.

---

4. Seeking reliable data on market trends, the *Financial Post* is by far the best source.

---

5. Who did you wish to speak to?

---

6. The keynote address will be delivered by Jeffrey Simpson, who is an author of popular books, and writes a column for "The Globe and Mail."

---

7. Often the reputation of an entire company depend on one employee that officially represents that company to the public.

---

8. The executive director, along with his staff, are working quickly to determine who should receive the Award.

---

9. Him and his co-workers, the top bowling team in the tournament, will represent our Company in the league finals on saturday.

---

10. Listening on the extension, details of the embezzlement plot were overheard by the Security Chief.

---

11. The acceptance of visa cards are in response to our customer's demand for a more efficient and convenient way of paying for parking here at Pearson International airport.

---

12. The human resources dept. interviewed dozens of people, they are seeking the better candidate for the opening.

---

13. Libraries' can be a challenging; yet lucrative market if you learn how to work the "system" to gain maximum visibility for you're products and services.

---

14. Either a supermarket or a discount art gallery are scheduled to open in the Mall.

---

15. I have told my supervisor that whomever shares my office with me cannot wear perfume, use spray deodorant, or other scented products.

Level 3: Document Critique

The following document may contain errors in grammar, capitalization, punctuation, abbreviation, number style, vocabulary, and spelling. You will also find errors that relate to planning and writing business messages. Concentrate on emphasizing the positive, being polite, using the "you" attitude to reflect your audience's viewpoint, and using bias-free language as you improve this memo. Correct all errors using standard proofreading marks (see the Correction Symbols list on p. 179).

MEMO

To: Blockbuster mngrs.

From: Sid Ryan, deputy chairmen, Viacom, Inc.

in care of Blockbuster Entertainment Canada

1201 Elm street; Toronto, ON M3P 2T6

Date October 8 2010

Sub: Recent Cash Flow and consumer response—Survey

Now that our stores have been re-organized with your hard work and cooperation, we hope revenues will rise to new heights; if we re-emphasize video rentals as Blockbusters core business and reduce the visibility of our sideline retail products. Just in case though, we want to be certain that these changes are having the postive affect on our cash flow that we all except and look forward to.

To help us make that determination, respond to the following survey questions and fax them back. Answer concisely; but use extra paper if necessary—for details and explanations.

When you finish the survey it will help headquarters improve service to you; but also, help us all improve service to our customers. Return your survay before before October 15 to my attention.

Then blockbuster hopefully can thrive in a marketplace, that critics say we cannot conquer. Blockbuster must choose wisely and serve it's customers well in a difficult video-rental business environment.

Times are very tough but if we work hard at it its possible we might make Blockbuster 'the man on the streets favourite 'place to go to rent videos!'

1.4 Adjectives

An adjective modifies (tells something about) a noun or pronoun. Each of the following phrases says more about the noun or pronoun than the noun or pronoun would say alone.

> an *efficient* staff   a *heavy* price
>
> *brisk* trade   *poor* you

Adjectives always tell us something that we wouldn't know without them. So you don't need to use adjectives when the noun alone, or a different noun, will give the meaning:

> a *company* employee
>
> (An employee ordinarily works for a company.)
>
> a *crate-type* container
>
> (*Crate* gives the entire meaning.)

Verbs in the *ing* (present participle) form can be used as adjectives:

> A *boring* job can sometimes turn into a *fascinating* career.

So can the past participle of verbs:

> A freshly *painted* house is a *sold* house.

Adjectives modify nouns more often than they modify pronouns. When adjectives do modify pronouns, however, the sentence usually has a linking verb:

> They were *attentive.*   It looked *appropriate.*
>
> He seems *interested.*   You are *skilful.*

At times, a series of adjectives precedes a noun:

> It was a *long* and *active* workday.

48

Such strings of adjectives are acceptable as long as each adjective contributes something distinctive.

Adjectives often pile up in front of a noun, like this:

> The *superficial, obvious* answer was the one she gave.

> The most valuable animal on the ranch is a *small black* horse.

That raises the question of whether a comma should be used to separate the adjectives. The answer is to use a comma when the two adjectives are coordinate—that is, when they act independently in modifying the noun. Do not use a comma when one of the adjectives is closely identified with (or even part of) the noun. In the first example above, the answer was *both* superficial *and* obvious, and therefore the two adjectives act independently. But in the second example, the *black horse* is small.

Another way to think about this is to use the word *and* as a replacement for the comma. Study the following example:

> We recommend a diet of leafy green vegetables.

> We recommend a diet of green, leafy vegetables.

Because some green vegetables are not leafy (cucumbers and zucchini, for example), it is correct to leave out the comma in the first example so that you know which kind of green vegetables are being discussed. But because all leafy vegetables are also green (green and leafy), the comma must be included in the second example.

You might also try switching the adjectives. If the order of the adjectives can be reversed without changing the meaning of the phrase, the adjectives are coordinate and you should use a comma. If the order cannot be reversed, you should not use a comma. Consider these examples:

> Here's our *simplified credit* application.

> Here's our *simplified, easy-to-complete* application.

Here's our *easy-to-complete, simplified* application.

A credit application may be simple or complex; however, you cannot talk about a credit, simplified application; therefore, leave the comma out of the first example. The application in the second and third examples is both simplified and easy to complete, no matter how you arrange the words, so include the comma in these examples.

1.4.1 Comparative Degree

Most adjectives can take three forms: simple, comparative, and superlative. The simple form modifies a single noun or pronoun. Use the comparative form when comparing two items. When comparing three or more items, use the superlative form.

Simple	Comparative	Superlative
hard	harder	hardest
safe	safer	safest
dry	drier	driest

The comparative form adds *er* to the simple form, and the superlative form adds *est*. (The *y* at the end of a word changes to *i* before the *er* or *est* is added.)

A small number of adjectives are irregular, including these:

Simple	Comparative	Superlative
good	better	best
bad	worse	worst
little	less	least

When the simple form of an adjective is two or more syllables, you usually add *more* to form the comparative and *most* to form the superlative:

Simple	Comparative	Superlative
useful	more useful	most useful
exhausting	more exhausting	most exhausting
expensive	more expensive	most expensive

The most common exceptions are two-syllable adjectives that end in *y:*

Simple	Comparative	Superlative
happy	happier	happiest
costly	costlier	costliest

If you choose this option, change the *y* to *i,* and tack *er* or *est* onto the end.

Some adjectives cannot be used to make comparisons because they themselves indicate the extreme. For example, if something is perfect, nothing can be more perfect. If something is unique or ultimate, nothing can be more unique or more ultimate.

1.4.2 Hyphenated Adjectives

Many adjectives used in the business world are actually combinations of words: *up-to-date* report, *last-minute* effort, *fifth-floor* suite, *well-built* engine. As you can see, they are hyphenated when they come before the noun they modify. However, when they come after the noun they modify, they are not hyphenated. In the following example, the adjectives appear in italics and the nouns they modify are underlined:

> The <u>report</u> is *up to date* because of our team's *last-minute* <u>efforts</u>.

Hyphens are not used when part of the combination is an adverb ending in *ly* (see Section 1.5).

> We live in a *rapidly shrinking* world.

> Our *highly motivated* employees will be well paid.

Hyphens are also omitted from word combinations that are used frequently.

Please consider renewing your *credit card* account.

Send those figures to our *data processing* department.

Our new intern is a *high school* student.

Improve Your Grammar, Mechanics, and Usage

Level 1: Self-Assessment—Adjectives

Review Section 1.4 and then look at the following 15 items. Answers to Level 1 exercises appear on page 166.

In items 1–5, fill in the appropriate form of the adjective that appears in parentheses:

1.   Of the two products, this one has the_____ (*great*) potential.

2.   The_____ (*perfect*) solution is *d.*

3.   Here is the_____ (*interesting*) of all the ideas I have heard so far.

4.   Our service is_____ (*good*) than theirs.

5.   The_____ (*hard*) part of my job is firing people.

In items 6–10, insert hyphens wherever required:

6.   A highly placed source revealed Dotson's last ditch efforts to cover up the mistake.

7.   Please send an extra large dust cover for my photocopier.

8.   A top secret document was taken from the president's office last night.

9.   A 30 year old person should know better.

10. If I write a large scale report, I want to know that it will be read by upper level management.

In items 11–15, insert required commas between adjectives:

11. The two companies are engaged in an all-out no-holds-barred struggle for dominance.

12. A tiny metal shaving is responsible for the problem.

13. She came to the office with a bruised swollen knee.

14. A chipped cracked sheet of glass is useless to us.

15. You'll receive our usual cheerful prompt service.

Level 2: Workplace Applications

The following items may contain errors in grammar, capitalization, punctuation, abbreviation, number style, and vocabulary. Rewrite each sentence in the space provided, correcting all errors. Write *C* in the space after any sentence that is already correct.

1. Its time that you learned the skills one needs to work with suppliers and vendors to get what you want and need.

2. Easy flexible wireless calling plans start for as little as $29 dollars a month.

3. There's several criteria used to select customer's to receive this offer.

4. PetFood Warehouse officially became PETsMART, Jim left the co. due to health reasons.

5. First quarter sales gains are evident in both the grocery store sector (up 1.03%) and the restaurant sector (up 3.17 percent) according to Food Institute estimates.

6.   Whatever your challenge, learning stronger "negotiating" tactics and strategies will improve the way people work and the results that comes from their efforts.

7.   To meet the increasing demand for Penta bottled-drinking-water, production capacity is being expanded by Bio-Hydration Research Lab by 80 percent.

8.   Seminars begin at 9 am and wrap up at 4:00 p.m.

9.   Burns Foods, a subsidiary of McCains has bought a facility in Scarborough, ON, that it will use to distribute products to customers such as convenience stores, stores that sell items at a discount, and mass merchants.

10.   The British Retail Consortium are releasing the 3rd edition of its Technical Standards on Apr. 22, reported the National Post.

11.   The reason SkillPath is the fastest growing training company in the world is because of our commitment to providing clients with the highest-quality learning experiences possible.

12.   According to professor Charles Noussair of the economics department of McGill University, opinion surveys "Capture the respondent in the role of a voter, not in the role of a consumer".

13.   The Study found that people, exposed to Purina banner ads, were almost 50 percent more likely to volunteer Purina as the first Dog Food brand that came to mind.

14.   In a consent decree with Health Canada, E'Ola International a dietary supplement maker agreed not to sell any more products containing the drug, ephedrine.

15.   Dennis Dickson is looking for a company both to make and distribute plaidberries under an exclusive licence, plaidberries is blackberries that are mixed with extracts and they are used as a filling.

Level 3: Document Critique

The following document may contain errors in grammar, capitalization, punctuation, abbreviation, number style, vocabulary, and spelling. You will also find errors that relate to writing business messages. Concentrate on emphasizing the positive, being polite, using the "you" attitude to reflect your audience's viewpoint, and using bias-free language as you improve this letter. Correct all errors using standard proofreading marks (see the Correction Symbols list on p. 179).

BURDETTE'S

• Special Sizes •

For Special Ladies and Gentlemen

820 Yonge Street, Toronto, ON   M5T 2T9 • (416) 967-5170 • Fax: (416) 967-1235
www.burdettes.com

10/19/09

Mrs. Bruce Crandall

1597 Church Street

Brantford, ON P3A 3V8

Dear Mrs. Crandall,

Order no. 89-97526-277

We were so happy to recieve your order—We know you'll be enjoying the dress you've selected from our fall catalogue. We feel its a popular number because its so versitile and flatters our heavier customers. We think you'll get alot of use out of it on your trip to Niagara Falls.

Unfortunately, you forgot to indicate what size you need. We can't ship your dress until you tell us your size. Plus, if you don't mail in the postage paid card that we've enclosed for you to use very soon we can't be guaranteeing that your attractive new dress will arrive in time for your trip!

Sincerely,

Melodie Proteau

1.5 Adverbs

An adverb modifies a verb, an adjective, or another adverb:

Modifying a verb:	Our marketing department works *efficiently*.
Modifying an adjective:	She was not dependable, although she was *highly* intelligent.
Modifying another adverb:	His territory was *too* broadly diversified, so he moved *extremely* cautiously.

Most of the adverbs in these examples are adjectives turned into adverbs by adding *ly,* which is how many adverbs are formed:

Adjective	Adverb
efficient	efficiently
extreme	extremely
high	highly
official	officially
separate	separately
special	specially

Some adverbs are made by dropping or changing the final letter of the adjective and then adding *ly:*

Adjective	Adverb
due	duly
busy	busily

Other adverbs don't end in *ly* at all. Here are a few examples of this type:

often	fast	too
soon	very	so

Some adverbs are difficult to distinguish from adjectives. For example, in the following sentences, is the underlined word an adverb or an adjective?

They worked <u>well</u>.

The baby is <u>well</u>.

In the first sentence, *well* is an adverb modifying the verb *worked*. In the second sentence, *well* is an adjective modifying the noun *baby*. To choose correctly between adverbs and adjectives, remember that verbs that describe a state of being link a noun to an adjective describing the noun. In contrast, you would use an adverb to modify an action verb.

Adjective	**Adverb**
He is a *good* worker.	He works *well*.
(What kind of worker is he?)	(How does he work?)
It is a *real* computer.	It *really* is a computer.
(What kind of computer is it?)	(To what extent is it a computer?)
The traffic is *slow*.	The traffic moves *slowly*.
(What quality does the traffic have?)	(How does the traffic move?)

1.5.1 Negative Adverbs

Negative adverbs (such as *neither, no, not, scarcely,* and *seldom*) are powerful words and therefore do not need any help in conveying a negative thought. In fact, using double negatives gives a strong impression of illiteracy, so avoid sentences like these:

I don't want no mistakes.

(Correct: "I don't want any mistakes," or "I want no mistakes.")

They couldn't hardly read the report.

(Correct: "They could hardly read the report," or "They couldn't read the report.")

They scarcely noticed neither one.

(Correct: "They scarcely noticed either one," or "They noticed neither one.")

1.5.2 Comparative Degree

Like adjectives, adverbs can be used to compare items. Generally, the basic adverb is combined with *more* or *most,* just as long adjectives are. However, some adverbs have one-word comparative forms:

One Item	Two Items	Three Items
quickly	more quickly	most quickly
sincerely	less sincerely	least sincerely
fast	faster	fastest
well	better	best

Practice Session: Adjectives and Adverbs

Underline the preferred choice within each set of parentheses in the following sentences. Answers to these exercises appear on page 167.

1. I always choose the (*less, least*) expensive brand.

2. Which would be (*better, best*), the store brand or the generic brand?

3.   This audit couldn't have come at a (*worse, worst*) time.

4.   When it comes to data analysis, Claire is (*more competent, competenter*) than Alexander.

5.   The ad agency's campaign for our new vitamin supplement is (*unique, very unique, most unique*), to say the least.

6.   A corporation can benefit from a (*well written, well-written*) annual report.

7.   The chairman's introductory message to the annual report was (*well written, well-written*).

8.   Even a (*beautifully written, beautifully-written*) report can be hampered by poor design and production.

9.   According to the Bank of Montreal, the number of (*credit-card, credit card*) applications has tripled in the past year.

10.   Angela wasn't feeling (*good, well*), so she went home early.

11.   Harrison and Martinez work (*good, well*) together.

12.   We are (*real, really*) excited about next week's product launch.

13.   Could this project be moving any more (*slow, slowly*) through the bureaucratic system?

14.   We (*could hardly, couldn't hardly*) wait to see how the brochure had turned out.

15.   Today TeKTech is (*more heavy, more heavily, most heavily*) involved in nanotechnology than five years ago.

Improve Your Grammar, Mechanics, and Usage

Level 1: Self-Assessment—Adjectives and Adverbs

Review Section 1.5 and then look at the following 15 items. Answers to Level 1 exercises appear on page 167.

In items 1–5, select the correct word (in italics), and write it in the space provided:

1.   Their performance has been _____ (*good/well*).

2.   I _____ (*sure/surely*) do not know how to help you.

3.   He feels _____ (*sick/sickly*) again today.

4.   Customs dogs are chosen because they smell _____ (*good/well*).

5.   The redecorated offices look _____ (*good/well*).

In items 6–10, provide the correct form of the adverb in parentheses:

6.   Which of the two programs computes (*fast*) _____?

7.   Kate has held 5 jobs over 13 years, and she was (*recently*) _____ employed by Graphicon.

8.   Could they be (*happily*) _____ employed than they are now?

9.   Of the two we have in stock, this model is the (*well*) _____ designed.

10.   Of all the arguments I've ever heard, yours is the (*logically*) _____ reasoned.

In items 11–15, rewrite the sentences to correct double negatives.

11. He doesn't seem to have none.

---

12. That machine is scarcely never used.

---

13. They can't get no replacement parts until Thursday.

---

14. It wasn't no different from the first event we promoted.

---

15. We've looked for it, and it doesn't seem to be nowhere.

Level 2: Workplace Applications

The following items may contain errors in grammar, capitalization, punctuation, abbreviation, number style, and vocabulary. Rewrite each sentence in the space provided, correcting all errors. Write *C* in the space after any sentence that is already correct.

1. All too often, whomever leaves the most out of his cost estimate is the one who wins the bid - if you can call it winning.

2. CEO, Dennis Kozlowski, called the plan to break up Safeco a 'mistake', considering the sluggish economy, spending cutbacks, and jitters on the Stock exchange over corporate accounting.

3. Shoppers were disinterested in the Web initially because many hyped services, offered no real cost or convenience advantages over offline stores.

4. Different jobs and different customers call for different pricing, estimating, and negotiating strategies.

5. Get to know the customer and their expectations, get the customer to talk about their primary use for you're product.

6. To homeowners, who feel they have found a competent contractor who has they're best interest's at heart, price will not matter nearly as much.

7. If I was you, I would of avoided investing in large conglomerates in light of the collapse of energy trader, Enron Corp., over accounting irregularities.

8. Outdoor goods retailer MEC has had significant, success with in-store kiosks that let customers choose between several types of merchandise.

9. To people in some areas of cyberspace "Advertising" is a four letter word but "Marketing" is perfectly acceptable.

10. In any business effort, making money requires planning. Strategic marketing, a good product, good customer service, considerable shrewdness—and much hard work.

11. Investors must decide weather to put their capitol into bonds or GICs.

12. Running at full capacity, millions of Nike shoes are being produced by manufacturing plants every day.

13. Metropolis' stationary has a picture of the CN tower on it.

14. Starbucks are planning to add fruit drinks to their menu in provinces throughout the west.

15. Credit ratings ain't what they used to be.

Level 3: Document Critique

The following document may contain errors in grammar, capitalization, punctuation, abbreviation, number style, vocabulary, and spelling. You will also find errors that relate to revising and completing your business messages. For example, as you improve this memo, look for the following:

- long words and phrases;

- redundancies—combinations of words that repeat the same idea;

- dangling modifiers—words or phrases that seem unconnected to the word or idea they are meant to modify; and

- camouflaged verbs—wordy noun forms that substitute for more powerful, direct verbs.

Also look for ways to impose parallelism, which is the use of similar (parallel) grammatical patterns to express similar ideas. Correct all errors using standard proofreading marks (see the Correction Symbols list on p. 179).

Memorandum

TO: Metro power Employees

FROM: sUSANNAH bEECH, hR aDMINISTRATOR

date: 22 September 2009

SUBJECT: Ways to improve your response to technology failures

Dear Metro Employees:

THere is always a chance of racing toward a deadline and suddenly having equipment fall. The following includes a few proposed suggestions to help you stave off, and cope with, technical equipment and system failures:

- Stay cool. There are many technical failures so they are commonplace in business; and it is likely that your bosses and co-workers will understand that you're having a prolbem and why.

- Practise preventive maintenance: Use cleaning cloths and sprays regularly, liquids and foods should be kept away from keyboards and printers; and you should make sure systems are shut down when you leave at night.

- The prompt reportage of computer failures to Bart Stone assistant director of information services ext. 2238, is important for faster repair asistance, who will get to your poblem as soon as it is humanely possible for him to do so, but: you must keep in mind that there are many people demanding his focused attention at any given time;

- If you suspect that a problem may be developing, don't wait until the crucial last moment to call for assistance.

- When a last-minute technical failure of equipment threatens to disrupt your composure you might want to consider the taking of a walk to calm down.

The last suggeston is perhaps the most important to keep your career on track. Lost tempers; taking out your feelings in violent outbursts, and rude language are threatening to co-workers and could result in a reprimand or other disciplinary action. By calling technical support lines for help, your equipment can stay in good working order and your temper will stay calm.

The timely implemention of repairs is important, so ask your supervisor for a list of support numbers to keep handy. Then, the next time you experience a technology giltch in your equipment or systems, there are going to be quite a few numbers handy for you to call to help you handle it as just another aspect of your business routine.

Sincerely,

Susannah Beech

Human Resources administrator

1.6 Other Parts of Speech

Nouns, pronouns, verbs, adjectives, and adverbs carry most of the meaning in a sentence. Four other parts of speech link them together in sentences: prepositions, conjunctions, articles, and interjections.

1.6.1 Prepositions

Prepositions are words like these:

of	to	for	with
at	by	from	about

Some prepositions consist of more than one word—like these:

because of	in addition to	out of	except for

And some prepositions are closely linked with a verb. When using verb-preposition combinations such as *look at* and *wipe out,* do not insert anything between the verb and the preposition (*Zara looked at the Web site; Julio looked at it too*). Other verb-preposition combinations, such as *look up,* can be split in some cases (*After Zara looked up the formula, Julio also looked it up*).

Prepositions begin prepositional phrases, which function like adjectives and adverbs by telling more about a pronoun, noun, or verb:

of a type   *by* Friday

to the point   *with* characteristic flair

To prevent misreading, prepositional phrases should be placed near the element they modify:

Of all our technicians, <u>she</u> is the best trained.

They couldn't see the <u>merit</u> *in my proposal.*

Someone left a <u>folder</u> *on my desk.*

It was once considered totally unacceptable to put a preposition at the end of a sentence. Now you may:

I couldn't tell what they were interested in.

What did she attribute it to?

However, be careful not to place prepositions at the end of sentences when doing so is unnecessary. In fact, avoid using any unnecessary preposition. In the following examples, the prepositions in parentheses should be omitted:

All (of) the staff members were present.

I almost fell off (of) my chair with surprise.

Where was Mr. Steuben going (to)?

They couldn't help (from) wondering.

The opposite problem is failing to include a preposition when you should. Consider the two sentences that follow:

Sales were more than $100 000 for Linda and Bill.

Sales were more than $100 000 for Linda and for Bill.

The first sentence indicates that Linda and Bill had combined sales over $100 000; the second, that Linda and Bill each had sales over $100 000, for a combined total in excess of $200 000. The preposition *for* is critical here.

Prepositions are also required in sentences like this one:

Which type of personal computer do you prefer?

Certain prepositions are used with certain words. When the same preposition is used with two or more words in a sentence, only the last preposition is required, as long as the meaning remains clear:

We are familiar (*with*) and satisfied *with* your company's products.

But when different prepositions are normally used with the words, all the prepositions must be included:

We are familiar *with* and interested *in* your company's products.

Here is an incomplete list of prepositions that have come to be used with particular words:

according to	different from	prior to
agree to (a proposal)	get from (receive)	reason with
agree with (a person)	get off (dismount)	responsible for
buy from	in accordance with	similar to
capable of	in search of	talk to (without interaction)
comply with	independent of	talk with (with interaction)
conform to	inferior to	wait for (person or thing)
differ from (things)	plan to	wait on (like a waiter)
differ with (person)	prefer to	

And here is a list of pairs of prepositions that are used in a particular way:

among/between: *Among* is used to refer to three or more (*Circulate the memo among the staff*); *between* refers to two (*Put the copy machine between Judy and Dan*) or, in some circumstances, to more than two.

as if/like: *As if* is used before a clause (see Section 1.6.2) (*It seems as if we should be doing something*); *like* is used before a noun or pronoun (*He seems like a nice guy*).

in/into: *In* is used to refer to a static position (*The file is in the cabinet*); *into* is used to refer to movement toward a position (*Put the file into the cabinet*).

Be sure to distinguish this pair of words:

have/of: *Have* is a verb used in verb phrases (*They should have checked first*); *of* is a preposition and is never used in such cases.

1.6.2 Conjunctions

Conjunctions connect the parts of a sentence: words, phrases, and clauses. You are probably most familiar with coordinating conjunctions such as the following:

and	for	or	yet
but	nor	so	

Conjunctions may be used to connect clauses (which have both a subject and a predicate—see Section 1.7) with other clauses, to connect phrases (which do not have both a subject and a predicate) with other phrases, and to connect words with words:

> We sell designer clothing *and* linens.
> (Words with words)

> Lara designs jewellery in her apartment *and* at our studio.
> (Phrases with phrases)

> I will call her on the phone today, *or* I will visit her office tomorrow.
> (Clauses with clauses)

Some conjunctions are used in pairs:

both . . . and   neither . . . nor   whether . . . or

either . . . or   not only . . . but also

With paired conjunctions, you must be careful to construct each phrase in the same way.

They *not only* <u>are out of</u> racquets *but also* <u>are out of</u> balls.

They are *not only* <u>out of</u> racquets *but also* <u>out of</u> balls.

They <u>are out of</u> *not only* racquets *but also* balls.

In other words, the construction that follows each part of the pair must be parallel, containing the same verbs, prepositions, and so on. The same need for parallelism exists when using conjunctions to join the other parts of speech:

He is listed in *either* <u>your</u> roster *or* <u>my</u> roster.

He is listed *neither* <u>in</u> your roster *nor* <u>on</u> the master list.

They *both* <u>gave</u> *and* <u>received</u> notice.

A certain type of conjunction is used to join a main (or independent) clause, which can stand on its own as a sentence, to one that is subordinate or dependent. Here is a partial list of conjunctions used to introduce dependent clauses:

although	before	once	unless
as soon as	even though	so that	until
because	if	that	when

Using conjunctions is also discussed in Sections 1.7.3 and 1.7.4.

1.6.3 Articles and Interjections

Only three articles exist in English: *the, a,* and *an.* These words are used, like adjectives, to specify which item you are talking about.

Interjections are words that express no solid information, only emotion:

Wow!   Well, well!

Oh, no!   Good!

Such purely emotional language has its place in private life and advertising copy, but it only weakens the effect of most business writing.

Practice Session: Prepositions, Conjunctions, and Articles

Circle the letter of the preferred choice in each pair of sentences. Answers to these exercises appear on page 168.

1. **a.** If we want to have the project done next week, we'll need those balance sheets by Wednesday.

    b. If we want to have the project done next week, by Wednesday we'll need those balance sheets.

2. **a.** From where did that information come?

    b. Where did that information come from?

3. **a.** Please look up the shipping rates for packages to France.

    b. Please look the shipping rates up for packages to France.

4. **a.** You need to indicate the type job you're seeking.

    b. You need to indicate the type of job you're seeking.

5. **a.** Michael got the technical data off of the Internet.

b. Michael got the technical data off the Internet.

6. a. When the meeting is over, Michelle will prepare the minutes.

b. When the meeting is over with, Michelle will prepare the minutes.

7. a. Sharon is familiar and knowledgeable about HTML coding.

b. Sharon is familiar with and knowledgeable about HTML coding.

8. a. We'll be deciding among the four applicants this afternoon.

b. We'll be deciding between the four applicants this afternoon.

9. a. Since Marshall isn't here, it looks like the conference call will have to be cancelled.

b. Since Marshall isn't here, it looks as if the conference call will have to be cancelled.

10. a. I would have had the memo done sooner, but my computer crashed.

b. I would of had the memo done sooner, but my computer crashed.

11. a. Once we have the survey results, we can put them in the report.

b. Once we have the survey results, we can put them into the report.

12. a. If you agree with the settlement, I can prepare the final papers.

b. If you agree to the settlement, I can prepare the final papers.

13. a. It is important that you provide not only your name but also your address and telephone number.

b. It is important that you provide not only your name but also address and telephone number.

14. a. The conference will be held in either March or July.

b. The conference will be held either in March or July.

15. a. Please prepare an RFP for the construction job.

    b. Please prepare a RFP for the construction job.

Improve Your Grammar, Mechanics, and Usage

Level 1: Self-Assessment—Prepositions and Conjunctions

Review Sections 1.6.1 and 1.6.2, and then look at the following items. Answers to Level 1 exercises appear on page168.

Rewrite items 1–5, deleting unnecessary words and prepositions, and adding required prepositions:

1.   Where was your argument leading to?

    _____

2.   I wish he would get off of the phone.

    _____

3.   This is a project into which you can sink your teeth.

    _____

4.   BMO Mercantile must become aware and sensitive to its customers' concerns.

    _____

5.   We are responsible for aircraft safety in the air, the hangars, and the runways.

    _____

In items 6–10, write the correct preposition in the blank:

6. Dr. Namaguchi will be talking _____ the marketing class, but she has no time for questions.

7. Matters like this are decided after thorough discussion _____ all seven department managers.

8. We can't wait _____ their decision much longer.

9. Their computer is similar _____ ours.

10. This model is different _____ the one we ordered.

In items 11–15, rewrite the sentences in the space provided to make phrases parallel:

11. She is active in not only a civic group but also in an athletic organization.

_____

12. That is either a mistake or was an intentional omission.

_____

13. The question is whether to set up a booth at the convention or be hosting a hospitality suite.

_____

14. We are doing better in both overall sales and in profits.

_____

15. She had neither the preferred educational background, nor did she have suitable experience.

_____

Level 2: Workplace Applications

The following items may contain errors in grammar, capitalization, punctuation, abbreviation, number style, and vocabulary. Rewrite each sentence in the space provided, correcting all errors. Write *C* in the space after any sentence that is already correct.

1. Peabody Energys commitment to environmental excellence is driven by the companies' mission statement which states that when mining is complete, the company will leave the land in a condition equal or better than it was before mining.

2. In 2009, Interco opened a state of the art distribution center in St. Thomas, Ontario, just South of the company's London, Ontario, Headquarters.

3. Miss Tucci was responsible for developing Terraspring's business plan, establishing the brand, and for launching the company.

4. The principle goals of the new venture will be to offer tailored financial products and meeting the needs of the community.

5. Nestle Waters North America are the number one bottled water company in Canada and the US.

6. The reason egg prices dropped sharply is because of a Post Easter reduction in demand.

7. Joining bank officials during the announcement of the program were Canadian member of parliament Alexina Robbins, Carlos Remirez, Mexican Ambassador to Canada, and "Don Francisco", the leading hispanic entertainment figure on the North American Continent.

8. The summer advertising campaign is the most unique in 7-Eleven's history.

9. Upon introducing it's new Quadruple Fudge flavour, consumers are expected to flock to Baskin-Robbins ice cream parlors.

10. The signing of a Trade Pact between the european union and Chile, is being delayed by european negotiators who insist the deal includes an agreement requiring Chile to stop using the names Cognac, Champagne, and Burgundy.

11. Canadian health advocate, Ms. Sheila F. Anthony called on the dietary supplement industry to institute better self regulation, and called on the media to refuse ads containing claims that are obviously false.

12. Founded in 1988, GSD&M has grown to become a nationally-acclaimed advertising agency with more than 500 employees and having billings of over $1 billion dollars.

13. Although marketing may seem to be the easier place to cut costs during a downturn its actually the last place you should look to make strategic cuts.

14. After closing their plant in Kelowna, Western Star Truck will have less than 200 employees.

15. The purchasing needs of professional's differ from blue collar workers.

Level 3: Document Critique

The following document may contain errors in grammar, capitalization, punctuation, abbreviation, number style, vocabulary, and spelling. You will also find errors relating to writing business letters, memos, and e-mail messages. For example, consider the format, organization, paragraph length, and subject line as you improve this memo. Correct all errors using standard proofreading marks (see the Correction Symbols list on p. 179).

Memo

To: George Kimball

From: John Mason

Subject: My trip back East

May 31, 2009

Dear George:

I went back to Montreal for apresentation the 15th of this month and I found it very informative. The sponsor of my visat was Vern Grouper. Vern is the Manager of the data processing-operation at headquarters; that is, their centralized data proceing operation. They've got quite a bit of power out there. And they do encourage us to utilize their capibilities, there services, and experiences to whatever extent will be beneficial to us. However, you could say it would be my observation that although they have a tremendous amount of computing capability that capability is directed toward a business dimension very different than ours and unlike anything we have. However, their are certain services that might be performed in our behalf by headquarters. For example, we could utilize people such as Vern to come and address our data-processing advisory group since I am planning on convening that group on a monthly basis.

By the way, I need to talk to you about the data-processing advicory group when you get a chance. I have 1 or 2 thoughts about some new approaches we can take with it I'd like to run by you if you don't mind. Its not too complicated just some simple ideas.

Let me know what you think of this idea about Vern coming here. If you like it than I will go ahead and set things in motion with Vern.

Sincerely,

John Mason

Supervisor

1.7 Sentences

Sentences are constructed with the major building blocks, the parts of speech.

Money talks.

This two-word sentence consists of a noun (*money*) and a verb (*talks*). When used in this way, the noun works as the first requirement for a sentence, the subject, and the verb works as the second requirement, the predicate. (The predicate is the part of the sentence that contains the verb; it may also be the verb itself.) Now look at this sentence:

They merged.

The subject in this case is a pronoun (*they*), and the predicate is a verb (*merged*). This is a sentence because it has a subject and a predicate. Here is yet another kind of sentence:

The plans are ready.

This sentence has a more complicated subject, consisting of the noun *plans* and the article *the;* the complete predicate is a verb that expresses a state of being (*are*) and an adjective (*ready*).

Without a subject (who or what does something) and a predicate (the doing of it), you have merely a collection of words, not a sentence.

1.7.1 Commands

In commands, the subject (always *you*) is only understood, not stated:

(You) Move your desk to the better office.

(You) Please try to finish by six o'clock.

1.7.2 Longer Sentences

More complicated sentences have more complicated subjects and predicates, but they still have a simple subject and a predicate verb. In the following examples, the subject is underlined once, the predicate verb twice:

<u>Marex</u> and <u>Contron</u> <u>enjoy</u> higher earnings each quarter.

(*Marex* [and] *Contron* do something; *enjoy* is what they do.)

My <u>interview</u>, coming minutes after my highway accident, <u>did</u> not <u>impress</u> or <u>move</u> anyone.

(*Interview* is what did something. What did it do? It *did* [not] *impress* [or] *move.*)

In terms of usable space, a steel <u>warehouse</u>, with its extremely long span of roof unsupported by pillars, <u>makes</u> more sense.

(*Warehouse* is what *makes.*)

These three sentences demonstrate several things. First, in all three sentences, the simple subject and predicate verb are the "bare bones" of the sentence, the parts that carry the core idea of the sentence. When trying to find the subject and predicate verb, disregard all prepositional phrases, modifiers, conjunctions, and articles.

Second, in the third sentence the verb is singular (*makes*) because the subject is singular (*warehouse*). Even though the plural noun *pillars* is closer to the verb, *warehouse* is the subject. So *warehouse* determines whether the verb is singular or plural. Subject and predicate must agree.

Third, the subject in the first sentence is compound (*Marex* [and] *Contron*). A compound subject, when connected by *and,* requires a plural verb (*enjoy*). Also in the second sentence, compound predicates are possible (*did* [not] *impress* [or] *move*).

Fourth, the second sentence incorporates a group of words—*coming minutes after my highway accident*—containing a form of a verb (*coming*) and a noun (*accident*). Yet this group of words is not a complete sentence for two reasons:

- Not all nouns are subjects: *Accident* is not the subject of *coming*.

- Not all verbs are predicates: A verb that ends in *ing* can never be the predicate of a sentence (unless preceded by a form of *to be,* as in *was coming*).

Because they don't contain a subject and a predicate, the words *coming minutes after my highway accident* (called a phrase) can't be written as a sentence. That is, the phrase cannot stand alone; it cannot begin with a capital letter and end with a period. So a phrase must always be just one part of a sentence.

Sometimes a sentence incorporates two or more groups of words that contain a subject and a predicate—which, as we have seen in Section 1.6.2, are known as clauses:

My *interview,* because *it* <u>came</u> minutes after my highway accident, <u>did</u> not <u>impress</u> or <u>move</u> anyone.

The independent clause is the portion of the sentence that could stand alone without revision:

My *interview* <u>did</u> not <u>impress</u> or <u>move</u> anyone.

The other part of the sentence could stand alone only by removing *because:*

(because) *It* <u>came</u> minutes after my highway accident.

This part of the sentence is known as a dependent clause; although it has a subject and a predicate (just as an independent clause does), it's linked to the main part of the sentence by a word (*because*) showing its dependence.

In summary, the two types of clauses—dependent and independent—both have a subject and a predicate. Dependent clauses, however, do not bear the main meaning of the sentence and are therefore linked to an independent clause. Nor can phrases stand alone, because they lack both a subject and a predicate. Only independent clauses can be written as sentences without revision.

1.7.3 Sentence Fragments

An incomplete sentence (a phrase or a dependent clause) that is written as though it were a complete sentence is called a fragment. Consider the following sentence fragments:

> Marilyn Sanders, having had pilferage problems in her store for the past year. Refuses to accept the results of our investigation.

This serious error can easily be corrected by putting the two fragments together:

> Marilyn Sanders, having had pilferage problems in her store for the past year, refuses to accept the results of our investigation.

Not all fragments can be corrected so easily. Here's more information on Sanders's pilferage problem.

> Employees a part of it. No authority or discipline.

Only the writer knows the intended meaning of those two phrases. Perhaps the employees are taking part in the pilferage. If so, the sentence should read:

> Some employees are part of the pilferage problem.

On the other hand, it's possible that some employees are helping with the investigation. Then the sentence would read:

> Some employees are taking part in our investigation.

It's just as likely, however, that the employees are not only taking part in the pilferage but are also being analyzed:

> Those employees who are part of the pilferage problem will accept no authority or discipline.

Even more meanings could be read into these fragments. Because fragments can mean so many things, they mean nothing. No well-written memo, letter, or report ever demands the reader to be an imaginative genius.

One more type of fragment exists, the kind represented by a dependent clause. Notice what *because* does to change what was once a unified sentence:

Our stock of sprinklers is depleted.

Because our stock of sprinklers is depleted.

Although the second version contains a subject and a predicate, adding *because* makes it a fragment. Words such as *because* form a special group of words called subordinating conjunctions. Here's a partial list:

after	if	unless
although	since	whenever
even if	though	while

When a word of this type begins a clause, the clause is dependent and cannot stand alone as a sentence. However, if a dependent clause is combined with an independent clause, it can convey a complete meaning. The independent clause may come before or after the dependent clause:

We are unable to fill your order because our stock of sprinklers is depleted.

Because our stock of sprinklers is depleted, we are unable to fill your order.

Also, to fix a fragment that is a dependent clause, remove the subordinating conjunction. Doing so leaves a simple but complete sentence:

Our stock of sprinklers is depleted.

The actual details of a situation will determine the best way for you to remedy a fragment problem.

The ban on fragments has one exception. Some advertising copy contains sentence fragments, written knowingly to convey a certain rhythm. Advertising is the only area of business in which fragments are acceptable.

1.7.4 Fused Sentences and Comma Splices

Just as there can be too little in a group of words to make it a sentence, there can also be too much:

All our mail is run through a postage meter every afternoon someone picks it up.

This example contains two sentences, not one, but the two have been blended so that it's hard to tell where one ends and the next begins. Is the mail run through a meter every afternoon? If so, the sentences should read:

All our mail is run through a postage meter every afternoon. Someone picks it up.

Perhaps the mail is run through a meter at some other time (morning, for example) and is picked up every afternoon:

All our mail is run through a postage meter. Every afternoon someone picks it up.

The order of words is the same in all three cases; sentence division makes all the difference. Either of the last two cases is grammatically correct. The choice depends on the facts of the situation.

Sometimes these so-called fused sentences have a more obvious point of separation:

Several large orders arrived within a few days of one another, too many came in for us to process by the end of the month.

Here the comma has been put between two independent clauses in an attempt to link them. When a lowly comma separates two complete sentences, the result is called a comma splice. A comma splice can be remedied in one of three ways:

- Replace the comma with a period and capitalize the next word: ". . . one another. Too many. . . ."

- Replace the comma with a semicolon and do not capitalize the next word: ". . . one another; too many. . . ." This remedy works only when the two sentences have closely related meanings.

- Change one of the sentences so that it becomes a phrase or a dependent clause. This remedy often produces the best writing, but it takes more work.

The third alternative can be carried out in several ways. One is to begin the blended sentence with a subordinating conjunction:

> Whenever several large orders arrived within a few days of one another, too many came in for us to process by the end of the month.

Another way is to remove part of the subject or the predicate verb from one of the independent clauses, thereby creating a phrase:

> Several large orders arrived within a few days of one another, too many for us to process by the end of the month.

Finally, you can change one of the predicate verbs to its *ing* form:

> Several large orders arrived within a few days of one another, too many coming in for us to process by the end of the month.

At other times a simple coordinating conjunction (such as *or, and,* or *but*) can separate fused sentences:

> You can fire them, or you can make better use of their abilities.

> Margaret drew up the designs, and Matt carried them out.

> We will have three strong months, but after that sales will taper off.

Be careful using coordinating conjunctions: Use them only to join sentences that express similar ideas.

Also, because they say relatively little about the relationship between the two clauses they join, avoid using coordinating conjunctions too often: *and* is merely an addition sign; *but* is just a turn signal; *or* only points to an alternative. Subordinating conjunctions such as *because* and *whenever* tell the reader a lot more.

1.7.5 Sentences with Linking Verbs

Linking verbs were discussed briefly in the section on verbs (Section 1.3). Here you can see more fully the way they function in a sentence. The following is a model of any sentence with a linking verb:

A (*verb*) B.

Although words such as *seems* and *feels* can also be linking verbs, let's assume that the verb is a form of *to be:*

A *is* B.

In such a sentence, A and B are always nouns, pronouns, or adjectives. When one is a noun and the other is a pronoun, or when both are nouns, the sentence says that one is the same as the other:

She is president.

Rachel is president.

When one is an adjective, it modifies or describes the other:

She is forceful.

Remember that when one is an adjective, it modifies the other as any adjective modifies a noun or pronoun, except that a linking verb stands between the adjective and the word it modifies.

1.7.6 Misplaced Modifiers

The position of a modifier in a sentence is important. The movement of *only* changes the meaning in the following sentences:

Only we are obliged to supply those items specified in your contract.

We are obliged only to supply those items specified in your contract.

We are obliged to supply only those items specified in your contract.

We are obliged to supply those items specified only in your contract.

In any particular set of circumstances, only one of those sentences would be accurate. The others would very likely cause problems. To prevent misunderstanding, place such modifiers as close as possible to the noun or verb they modify.

For similar reasons, whole phrases that are modifiers must be placed near the right noun or verb. Mistakes in placement create ludicrous meanings.

Antia Information Systems has bought new computer chairs for the programmers *with more comfortable seats*.

The anatomy of programmers is not normally a concern of business writers. Obviously, the comfort of the chairs was the issue:

Antia Information Systems has bought new computer chairs *with more comfortable seats* for the programmers.

Here is another example:

I asked him to file all the letters in the cabinet that had been answered.

In this ridiculous sentence the cabinet has been answered, even though no cabinet in history is known to have asked a question.

That had been answered is too far from *letters* and too close to *cabinet*. Here's an improvement:

I asked him to file in the cabinet all the letters that had been answered.

In some cases, instead of moving the modifying phrase closer to the word it modifies, the best solution is to move the word closer to the modifying phrase.

Practice Session: Sentences

Circle the letter of the preferred choice in each group of sentences. Answers to these exercises appear on page 169.

1. **a.** Cyberterrorism—orchestrated attacks on a company's information systems for political or economic purposes—is a very real threat.

   b. Cyberterrorism—orchestrated attacks on a company's information systems for political or economic purposes—are a very real threat.

2. **a.** E-mail, phone calls, and faxes, each one a distraction, interrupts employees when they work.

   b. E-mail, phone calls, and faxes, each one a distraction, interrupt employees when they work.

3. **a.** About 35 percent of major Canadian companies keep tabs on workers. Because they want to protect valuable company information.

   b. About 35 percent of major Canadian companies keep tabs on workers, because they want to protect valuable company information.

   c. About 35 percent of major Canadian companies keep tabs on workers; because they want to protect valuable company information.

4. **a.** Despite its small size and relative isolation in the Arctic Circle. Finland leads the pack in mobile phone technology and its applications.

   b. Despite its small size and relative isolation in the Arctic Circle; Finland leads the pack in mobile phone technology and its applications.

   c. Despite its small size and relative isolation in the Arctic Circle, Finland leads the pack in mobile phone technology and its applications.

5. **a.** Many employees erroneously believe that their e-mail and voice mail messages are private they're surprised when e-mail ends up in places where they did not intend it to go.

   b. Many employees erroneously believe that their e-mail and voice mail messages are private, they're surprised when e-mail ends up in places where they did not intend it to go.

   c. Many employees erroneously believe that their e-mail and voice mail messages are private, so they're surprised when e-mail ends up in places where they did not intend it to go.

6. **a.** Each day countless Canadians walk through the doors of a Tim Hortons, they line up to buy coffee and doughnuts.

   b. Each day countless Canadians walk through the doors of a Tim Hortons, lining up to buy coffee and doughnuts.

7. **a.** The chain won its earliest fans for its promise of freshly brewed coffee and its wide selection of doughnuts, many customers like to come for a bowl of soup and a sandwich.

   b. The chain won its earliest fans for its promise of freshly brewed coffee and its wide selection of doughnuts; many customers like to come for a bowl of soup and a sandwich.

   c. The chain won its earliest fans for its promise of freshly brewed coffee and its wide selection of doughnuts. But many customers like to come for a bowl of soup and a sandwich.

8. **a.** Responding to popular demand, outlets have been opened by Tim Hortons on some Canadian military bases, including an airfield in Afghanistan.

   b. Responding to popular demand, on some Canadian military bases, including an airfield in Afghanistan, Tim Hortons outlets have been opened.

   c. Responding to popular demand, Tim Hortons has opened outlets on some Canadian military bases, including an airfield in Afghanistan.

88

9. **a.** All Rocky Mountain Cycles' bikes are custom-made in the factory to meet the rider's size and component preferences.

   b. All Rocky Mountain Cycles' bikes are custom-made to meet the rider's size and component preferences in the factory.

10. **a.** Catering to its customers, about 2000 bikes are built annually by Rocky Mountain Cycles.

   b. Catering to its customers, about 2000 bikes are built by Rocky Mountain Cycles annually.

   c. Catering to its customers, Rocky Mountain Cycles builds about 2000 bikes annually.

2.0 Punctuation

On the highway, signs tell you when to slow down or stop, where to turn, when to merge. In similar fashion, punctuation helps readers negotiate your prose. The proper use of punctuation keeps readers from losing track of your meaning.

2.1 Periods

Use a period (1) to end any sentence that is not a question, (2) with certain abbreviations, and (3) between dollars and cents in an amount of money.

2.2 Question Marks

Use a question mark after any direct question that requests an answer:

> Are you planning to enclose a cheque, or shall we bill you?

Don't use a question mark with commands phrased as questions for the sake of politeness:

> Will you send us a cheque today.

2.3 Exclamation Points

Use exclamation points after highly emotional language. Because business writing almost never calls for emotional language, you will seldom use exclamation points.

2.4 Semicolons

Semicolons have three main uses. One is to separate two closely related independent clauses:

> The outline for the report is due within a week; the report itself is due at the end of the month.

A semicolon should also be used instead of a comma when the items in a series have commas within them:

Our previous meetings were on November 11, 2007; February 20, 2008; and April 28, 2009.

Finally, a semicolon should be used to separate independent clauses when the second one begins with a word such as *however, therefore,* or *nevertheless* or a phrase such as *for example* or *in that case:*

Our supplier has been out of part D712 for 10 weeks; however, we have found another source that can ship the part right away.

His test scores were quite low; on the other hand, he has a lot of relevant experience.

Section 4.4 has more information on using transitional words and phrases.

2.5 Colons

Use a colon after the salutation in a business letter. You also use a colon at the end of a sentence or phrase introducing a list or (sometimes) a quotation:

Our study included the three most critical problems: insufficient capital, incompetent management, and inappropriate location.

In some introductory sentences, phrases such as *the following* or *that is* are implied by using a colon.

A colon should not be used when the list, quotation, or idea is a direct object or part of the introductory sentence:

We are able to supply

staples

wood screws

nails

toggle bolts

This shipment includes 9 videotapes, 12 CDs, and 14 cassette tapes.

Another way you can use a colon is to separate the main clause and another sentence element when the second explains, illustrates, or amplifies the first:

> Management was unprepared for the union representatives' demands: this fact alone accounts for their arguing well into the night.

However, in contemporary usage, such clauses are frequently separated by a semicolon.

Practice Session: Punctuation 1

Circle the letter of the preferred choice in the following groups of sentences. Answers to these exercises appear on page 169.

1. **a.** She asked me whether we should increase our insurance coverage?

    b. She asked me whether we should increase our insurance coverage.

2. **a.** Would you please let me know when the copier is free.

    b. Would you please let me know when the copier is free?

3. **a.** You won't want to miss this exciting seminar!

    b. You won't want to miss this exciting seminar.

4. **a.** The officers of the board of directors arc John Rogers, president, Robin Doug Donlan, vice-president for programming, Bill Pittman, vice-president for operations, and Mary Sturhann, secretary.

b. The officers of the board of directors are John Rogers, president; Robin Doug Donlan, vice-president for programming; Bill Pittman, vice-president for operations; and Mary Sturhann, secretary.

c. The officers of the board of directors are John Rogers, president; Robin Doug Donlan, vice-president for programming; Bill Pittman, vice-president for operations, and Mary Sturhann, secretary.

5. **a.** Cancorps is the best brokerage house in Canada; it's got more offices than any other brokerage house.

b. Cancorps is the best brokerage house in Canada, it's got more offices than any other brokerage house.

6. **a.** One of the VSE's top priorities is to crack down on insider trading, however it readily admits that it has more work to do in this area.

b. One of the VSE's top priorities is to crack down on insider trading; however, it readily admits that it has more work to do in this area.

7. **a.** To keep on top of financial news, you should consult publications aimed specifically at investors, such as *Report on Business* and *Canadian Business*.

b. To keep on top of financial news, you should consult publications aimed specifically at investors; such as, *Report on Business* and *Canadian Business*.

c. To keep on top of financial news, you should consult newspapers aimed specifically at investors; such as *Report on Business* and *Canadian Business*.

8. **a.** Dear Dr. Schatzman,

b. Dear Dr. Schatzman:

9. **a.** The three basic concepts that guide accountants are: the fundamental accounting equation, double-entry bookkeeping, and the matching principle.

b. The three basic concepts that guide accountants are the fundamental accounting equation, double-entry bookkeeping, and the matching principle.

c. The three basic concepts that guide accountants are the fundamental accounting equation; double-entry bookkeeping; and the matching principle.

10. a. Accountants are guided by three basic concepts, the fundamental accounting equation, double-entry bookkeeping, and the matching principle.

b. Accountants are guided by three basic concepts: the fundamental accounting equation; double-entry bookkeeping; and the matching principle.

c. Accountants are guided by three basic concepts: the fundamental accounting equation, double-entry bookkeeping, and the matching principle.

Improve Your Grammar, Mechanics, and Usage

Level 1: Self-Assessment—Periods, Question Marks, and Exclamation Points

Review Sections 2.1, 2.2, and 2.3, and then look at the following 15 items. Answers to Level 1 exercises appear on page 170.

In items 1–15, add periods, question marks, and exclamation points wherever they are appropriate.

1. Dr Eleanor H Hutton has requested information on TaskMasters, Inc

2. That qualifies us as a rapidly growing new company, don't you think

3. Our president, Daniel Gruber, is a CGA On your behalf, I asked him why he started the company

4. In the past three years, we have experienced phenomenal growth of 800 percent

5. Contact me at 1358 N Bluff Avenue, Lethbridge, AB T1K 1L6

6. Jack asked, "Why does he want to know Maybe he plans to become a competitor"

7. The debt load fluctuates with the movement of the Bank of Canada prime rate

8. I can't believe we could have missed such a promising opportunity

9. Is consumer loyalty extinct Yes and no

10. Johnson and Kane, Inc has gone out of business What a surprise

11. Will you please send us a cheque today so that we can settle your account

12. Mr James R Capp will be our new CEO, beginning January 20, 2010

13. The rag doll originally sold for $998, but we have lowered the price to a mere $599

14. Will you be able to make the presentation at the conference, or should we find someone else

15. So I ask you, "When will we admit defeat" Never

Level 2: Workplace Applications

The following items may contain errors in grammar, capitalization, punctuation, abbreviation, number style, and vocabulary. Rewrite each sentence in the space provided, correcting all errors. Write *C* in the space after any sentence that is already correct.

1. Attached to both the transit station and the Fairmont hotel, one doesn't even need to step outside the convention centre to go from train to meeting room.

2. According to national statistics, 61 percent of that countries employers have less than 5 workers.

3. "The problem", said Business Owner Mike Millorn, "Was getting vendor's of raw materials to take my endeavour serious."

4. After pouring over trade journals, quizzing industry experts, and talks with other snack makers, the Harpers' decided to go in the pita chip business.

5. A Mac with half as much RAM and a slower processor is as fast or faster than a PC.

6. The couple has done relatively little advertising, instead they give away samples in person at trade shows, cooking demonstrations, and in grocery stores.

7. CME Information Services started by videotaping doctor's conventions, and selling the recorded presentations to nonattending physicians that wanted to keep track of the latest developments.

8. For many companies, the two biggest challenges to using intranets are: getting people to use it and content freshness.

9. Company meetings including 'lunch and learn' sessions are held online often.

10. Most Children's Orchard franchisees, are women between the ages of 30-50; first time business owners lacking even basic computer skills.

11. Joining the company in 2006, she had watched it expand and grow from a single small office to a entire floor of a skyscraper.

12. One issue that effected practically everyone was that they needed to train interns.

13. The Web site includes information on subjects as ordinary as the filling out of a federal express form, and as complex as researching a policy issue.

14. "Some management theories are good, but how many people actually implement them the right way?", says Jack Hartnett President of D. L. Rogers Corp..

15. Taking orders through car windows, customers are served by roller-skating servers at Sonic restaurants.

Level 3: Document Critique

The following document may contain errors in grammar, capitalization, punctuation, abbreviation, number style, vocabulary, and spelling. You will also find errors relating to writing positive business messages, a category that includes routine, good-news, and goodwill messages. For example, consider the organization and relevance of material as you improve this routine request for information. Correct all errors using standard proofreading marks (see the Correction Symbols list on p. 179).

Risa Zenaili

883 Rue St. Hubert Aven.

Chicoutimi, PC G7H 1Z6

418-555-9983

rzenaili@bellca.net

March 13 2009

Tharita Jones Owner

Subway Restaurant

120 Boulevard Cité des Jeunes

Chicoutimi, QC G8P 2A4

Dear Ms. Jones,

I am investigatting careers in vareous fast-food enviroments, since I expect to complete my degree in business administration within the next 3 years and that should leave me enough time to grow into a management position. Subway gave me your name when I asked for a franchise owner who might be willing to answer some questions about managment careers with the

---

company. You may be able to provide the kind of informaton I'll never get from coporate brochures.

For example I'd like to know how long I can expect to work at an entry level before promotions are considered. How many levels must I rise before reaching assistant manager. And how many before I would be considered as manager, assuming I've performed well. Sometimes a person is promoted because they are qualified and sometimes it just because they willing to work long hours, so I want to know this before I commit myself!

I'm looking for a company that will offer me the best future in the most promising environment and since there are so many to choose from I am trying to be very careful in making this choice. I'd be really gratefull if you could take a moment to share any advice or encouragment you might have for me because as you know this kind of decision is one we all must make one day and it will effect us for a long, long time to come

I also like to know: How many hour a week can I expect to work to be on management career track? Once I reach management level: will those hours increase?

What qualifications do you look for in your managers and assitant managers? Plus: Benefits the company offers, special training—availibility and qualifications; how to improve my chances for promation if I choose Subway?

Please let me hear from you before the end of the month.

If you prefer to call than write; you reach me at 418 555-9983 day or evening. My cellphone number is (418) 555-8838. Or you can send a reply to me at the address above or to my e-mail address rzeinali@bellca.net

Sincerely:

Risa Zeinali

2.6 Commas

Commas have many uses; the most common is to separate items in a series:

> He took the job, learned it well, worked hard, and succeeded.

> Put paper, pencils, and paper clips on the requisition list.

Company style often dictates omitting the final comma in a series. However, if you have a choice, use the final comma (called a series comma or serial comma); it's often necessary to prevent misunderstanding.

A second place to use a comma is between independent clauses that are joined by a coordinating conjunction (*and, but,* or *or*) unless one or both are very short:

> She spoke to the sales staff, and he spoke to the production staff.

> I was advised to proceed and I did.

A third use for the comma is to separate a dependent clause at the beginning of a sentence from an independent clause:

> Because of our lead in the market, we may be able to risk introducing a new product.

However, a dependent clause at the end of a sentence is separated from the independent clause by a comma only when the dependent clause is unnecessary to the main meaning of the sentence:

> We may be able to introduce a new product, although it may involve some risk.

A fourth use for the comma is after an introductory phrase or word:

> Starting with this amount of capital, we can survive in the red for one year.

Through more careful planning, we may be able to serve more people.

> Yes, you may proceed as originally planned.

However, with short introductory prepositional phrases and some one-syllable words (such as *hence* and *thus*), the comma is often omitted:

Before January 1 we must complete the inventory.

Thus we may not need to hire anyone.

In short the move to Winnipeg was a good idea.

Fifth, commas are used to surround nonrestrictive phrases or words (expressions that can be removed from the sentence without changing the meaning):

The new owners, the Kowacks, are pleased with their purchase.

Sixth, commas are used between coordinate adjectives modifying the same noun (see Section 1.4):

She left Monday for a long, difficult recruiting trip.

To test the appropriateness of such a comma, try reversing the order of the adjectives: *a difficult, long recruiting trip.* If the order cannot be reversed, leave out the comma (*a good old friend* isn't the same as *an old good friend*). A comma is also not used when one of the adjectives is part of the noun. Compare these two phrases:

a distinguished, well-known figure

a distinguished public figure

The adjective-noun combination of *public* and *figure* has been used together so often that it has come to be considered a single thing: *public figure.* So no comma is required.

Seventh, commas are used both before and after the year in sentences that include month, day, and year:

It will be sent by December 15, 2009, from our Windsor plant.

Some companies write dates in another form: 15 December 2009. No commas should be used in that case. Nor is a comma needed when only the month and year are present (December 2009).

Eighth, commas are used to set off a variety of parenthetical words and phrases within sentences, including province names, dates, abbreviations, transitional expressions, and contrasted elements:

> They were, in fact, prepared to submit a bid.
>
> Our best programmer is Ken, who joined the company just a month ago.
>
> Habermacher, Inc., went public in 2006.
>
> Our goal was increased profits, not increased market share.
>
> Service, then, is our main concern.
>
> The factory was completed in Fredericton, New Brunswick, just three weeks ago.
>
> Joanne Dubiik, M.D., has applied for a loan from RBC.
>
> I started work here on March 1, 2008, and soon received my first promotion.

Ninth, a comma is used to separate a quotation from the rest of the sentence:

> Your warranty reads, "These conditions remain in effect for one year from date of purchase."

However, the comma is left out when the quotation as a whole is built into the structure of the sentence:

> He hurried off with an angry "Look where you're going."

Finally, a comma should be used whenever it's needed to avoid confusion or an unintended meaning. Compare the following:

> Ever since they have planned new ventures more carefully.
>
> Ever since, they have planned new ventures more carefully.

Improve Your Grammar, Mechanics, and Usage

Level 1: Self-Assessment—Semicolons, Colons, and Commas

Review Sections 2.4, 2.5, and 2.6, and then look at the following 15 items. Answers to Level 1 exercises appear on page 170.

In items 1–15, insert all required semicolons, colons, and commas:

1. This letter looks good that one doesn't.

2. I want to make one thing perfectly clear neither of you will be promoted if sales figures don't improve.

3. The Zurich airport has been snowed in therefore I won't be able to meet with you before January 4.

4. His motivation was obvious to get Meg fired.

5. Only two firms have responded to our survey J. J. Perkins and Tucker & Tucker.

6. Send a copy to Mary Kwan Marketing Director Robert Bache Comptroller and Dennis Mann Sales Director.

7. Please be sure to interview these employees next week Henry Gold Doris Hatch and George Iosupovich.

8. We have observed your hard work because of it we are promoting you to manager of your department.

9. You shipped three items on June 7 however we received only one of them.

10. The convention kit includes the following response cards, giveaways, brochures, and a display rack.

11. The workers wanted an immediate wage increase they had not had a raise in nearly two years.

12. This, then, is our goal for 2011 to increase sales 35 percent.

13. His writing skills are excellent however he still needs to polish his management style.

14. We would like to address three issues efficiency profitability and market penetration.

15. Remember this rule When in doubt, leave it out.

Level 2: Workplace Applications

The following items may contain errors in grammar, capitalization, punctuation, abbreviation, number style, and vocabulary. Rewrite each sentence in the space provided, correcting all errors. Write *C* in the space after any sentence that is already correct.

1. Hector's, Julie's, and Tim's report was well-received by the Committee.

2. Everyone who are interested in signing up for the training seminar must do so by 3:00 o'clock PM on friday.

3. David Stern is a management and training expert that has spent a major part of his career coaching, counselling, and giving advise both to managers and workers.

4. Be aware and comply with local "zoning ordnances" and building codes.

5. Garrett didn't seem phased when her supervisor didn't except her excuse for being late, she forgot to set her alarm.

6. Copyright laws on the Internet is not always clearly defined, be sure your research doesn't extend to "borrowing" a competitors' keywords or copy.

7. Sauder Woodworking, in Sydney, NS, sell a line of ready to assemble computer carts, desks, file cabinets, and furniture that is modular that can be mixed and matched to meet each business owners' personal taste.

8. Spamming is the most certain way to loose you're e-mail account, Web site, and you're reputation.

9. Us programmers have always tried to help others learn the tricks of the trade, especially Roger and myself.

10. The person whom was handling Miss Gill's account told her that an error had been made by the bank in her favour.

11. "The trouble with focus groups" says Marketing Expert Frances Knight, "Is that consumers rarely act in real life they way they do in a "laboratory" setting."

12. In a industry in which design firms tend to come and go Skyline has licensed seventy products and grown to 8 employees.

13. If youv'e ever wondered why fast food restaurants are on the left and gift shops are on the right as you walk toward the gate into a newly-constructed airport you should read Malcolm Gladwells article, 'The Science of Shopping,' in the *New Yorker*.

14. Anyone whose starting a business should consider using their life story, as a way to generate customer's interest.

15. Having been in business since 2002, over 1000s of sales calls has been made by Mr. Jurzang to contact prospects for his bi-lingual business services.

Level 3: Document Critique

The following document may contain errors in grammar, capitalization, punctuation, abbreviation, number style, vocabulary, and spelling. You may also discover problems with wordiness, usage, and appropriateness of tone for bad-news messages. Correct all errors using standard proofreading marks (see the Correction Symbols list on p. 179).

MEMORANDUM

To: all employees

Subject: Health insurance—Changes

Date: Octbr. 22, 2009

From: Lucinda Goodman, Benefits Mangr., Human resources

Unlike many companies, Bright Manufacturing has always paid a hundred % of dental insurance for it's employees, absorbing the recent 10-20 percent annual cost increases in order to provide this important benefit. This year; Maritime Life gave us some terrible news: the cost increase for our employee's dental coverage would be a staggering fourty percent per month next year

To mange the increase and continue to offer you and your family highquality health coverage we have negotiated several changes with Maritime Life; a new cost saving alternative is also being offered by us:

1. Under the Maritime Life Plus plan, copay amounts for office visits will be ten dollars next year/ $50 for emergency dental visits.

2. 80% of employees' insurance coverage (including 10 percent of the cost increase) will be paid by Bright next year and 100 % of the cost of dentures and dental implants (including a 23 percent cost increase). The remaining twenty percent of dental coverage will be deducted by us monthly from your salary, if you choose to remain on a Maritime Life Plus plan. We realize this is alot, but its still less than many companies charge their employees.

3. A fully paid alternative dental plan, Maritime Life, will now be provided by Bright at no cost to employees. But be warned that there is a deadline. If you want to switch to this new plan you must do so during our open enrollment period, Nov. 20 to December 1 2009, and we will not consder applications for the change after that time so don't get your forms in late.

There are forms available in the Human Resources office for changing your coverage. They must be returned between November 20 and December 1, 2009. If you wish to remain on a Maritime Life Plus policy, you do not need to notify us; payroll deductions for company employees on the plan will occur automatic beginning January first, 2010.

If you have questions, please call our new Health Benefits Information line at ext. 3392. Our Intranet sight will also provide you easy with information about dental care coverage online if you click the "Health Benefits" icon. Since our founding in 1964, we have provided our company employees with the best health coverage available. We all hate rising costs and although things are looking bleak for the future but we're doing all we can do to hold on to this helpful benefit for you.

Level 1: Self-Assessment—Commas

Review Section 2.6 and then look at the following 15 items. Answers to Level 1 exercises appear on page 171.

In items 1–15, insert required commas:

1. Please send us four cases of filters two cases of wing nuts and a bale of rags.

2. Your analysis however does not account for returns.

3. As a matter of fact she has seen the figures.

4. Before May 7 2008 they wouldn't have minded either.

5. After Martha has gone talk to me about promoting her.

6. Stoneridge Inc. will go public on September 9 2012.

7. We want the new copier not the old model.

8. "Talk to me" Sandra said "before you change a thing."

9. Because of a previous engagement Dr. Stoeve will not be able to attend.

10. The company started attracting attention during the long hard recession of the mid-1970s.

11. You can reach me at this address: 717 Darby Place Summerside PE C1N 3T4.

12. Transfer the documents from Sherbrooke Quebec to Don Mills Ontario.

13. Sam O'Neill the designated representative is gone today.

14. With your help we will soon begin.

15. She may hire two new representatives or she may postpone filling those territories until spring.

Level 2: Workplace Applications

The following items may contain errors in grammar, capitalization, punctuation, abbreviation, number style, and vocabulary. Rewrite each sentence in the space provided, correcting all errors. Write *C* in the space after any sentence that is already correct.

1. A pitfall of internal promotions is, that a person may be given a job beyond their competence.

2. What makes this development possible is the technological advances in todays workplace.

3. We have up to date physical safeguards, such as secure areas in buildings, electronic safeguards, such as passwords and secure codes, and we have procedural safeguards, such as customer authentication procedures.

4. When asked why BASF need to bring in a consultant after so many years, process development quality assurance manager Merritt Sink says that experience is extremely important on these type of projects.

5. Looking at just one growth indicator two-way trade between Canada and China "ballooned" to $25 billion in 2003; and expanded another 50 percent in 2004.

6.   Levi Strauss was the first major manufacturer to develop and do publicity about a formal Code of Conduct for it's contract manufacturers.

7.   In foreign countries, while the local labour laws may be comparable or even more strict than in Canada, law enforcement mechanisms are weak or nonexistent often.

8.   Hyundai Motor Co., South Koreas' largest-automotive producer are looking for a North-American site to build a $1 billion assembly and manufacturing plant.

9.   The long term success of some Internet products rest heavily on the Webs ability to guarantee payment security and privacy.

10.   Being creative, flexibility, and dynamic planning are the critical elements of any successful, manufacturing process.

11.   "Starbucks expanded the Frappucciono family to satisfy customers by offering a broader array of blended beverages," said Howard Behar, Starbucks president, North American Operations.

12.   Internationally-renowned interior designer, Jacques Garcia will be designing the hotel's interiors; the gardens will also be designed by him.

13.   Anyone who thinks they know what a CEO does is probably wrong, according to Eric Kriss; a professional Chief Executive.

14.   Michael Walker, who founded the Fraser institute, headquartered in Vancouver, Brit Col has spent decade's studying economics.

15.   The best job-description in the world wont provide you with a trusted executive, finely-honed interviewing skills only will help one do that.

Level 3: Document Critique

The following document may contain errors in grammar, capitalization, punctuation, abbreviation, number style, vocabulary, and spelling. You may also discover problems with wordiness, usage, organization, and tone for a sales message. Correct all errors using standard proofreading marks (see the Correction Symbols list on p. 179).

Date: Monday, 22 June 2010

From: Sasha Morgenstern

To:

Subject: Insurence Service

Dear potential buyers:

You will be able to compare prices from more than three hundredinsurance companies'. Or find the lower rates for any insurance, such as Term life Automobile; Medical. dental. "No-exam" whole life, workers' compensation, Medicare supplements; Fixed annuities

$500 Dollar Guaranttes

We'll find you the lowest rates for term life insurance, or we'll deliver $500 to you overnight. Plus, every quote will carry a $five hundred dollar guarrantee of uptotheday accurracy.

"Quotesmith.com provides rock-bottom quotes."—The Globe & Mail

All quotes are free and accurrate;

We offer Lightning-Fast ServicE

What their saying about us can be found at www.quotesmith.com. Our speedy service is being talked about by everyone, which has received high ratings and postive reviews from "Report on Business" "BC Business" "Toronto Star"

EXPERT ADVISE WILL BE PROVIDED WITH NO SALES PITCH:

You will not be dealing with insurance agents to save you time and money. But if you want advise our saleried insurance experts are available at our toll-free customer service number. We hope you will take a moment to peruse our webstie, www.quotesmith.com today if possible.

Very truly yours,

Sasha Morgenstern

2.7 Dashes

Use a dash to surround a comment that is a sudden turn in thought:

> Membership in the ITVA—it's expensive but worth it—may be obtained by applying to our Vancouver office.

A dash can also be used to emphasize a parenthetical word or phrase:

> Third-quarter profits—in excess of $2 million—are up sharply.

Finally, use dashes to set off a phrase that contains commas:

> All our offices—Calgary, Mississauga, and Moncton—have sent representatives.

Don't confuse a dash with a hyphen. A dash separates and emphasizes words, phrases, and clauses more strongly than a comma or parentheses can; a hyphen ties two words so tightly that they almost become one word.

Most computer fonts let you use the em dash symbol. When typing a dash in e-mail, type two hyphens with no space before, between, or after.

2.8 Hyphens

Hyphens are mainly used in three ways. The first is to separate the parts of compound words beginning with such prefixes as *self-, ex-, quasi-,* and *all-:*

self-assured	quasi-official
ex-supervisor	all-important

However, omit hyphens from and close up most words that have prefixes such as *re, un,* and *inter:*

reorganize	unconnected	interdepartmental

Use a hyphen when (1) the prefix occurs before a proper noun or (2) the vowel at the end of the prefix is the same as the first letter of the root word:

inter-European   re-entry

anti-inflammatory   extra-atmospheric

When in doubt, consult your dictionary.

Hyphens are also used in some compound adjectives, which are adjectives made up of two or more words. Specifically, you should use hyphens in compound adjectives that come before the noun:

an interest-bearing account   well-informed executives

However, you need not hyphenate when the adjective follows a linking verb:

This account is interest bearing.

Their executives are well informed.

You can shorten sentences that list similar hyphenated words by dropping the common part from all but the last word:

Check the costs of first-, second-, and third-class postage.

Finally, hyphens may be used to divide words at the end of a typed line. Such hyphenation is best avoided, but when you have to divide words at the end of a line, do so correctly (see Section 3.4). A dictionary will show how words are divided into syllables.

112

2.9 Apostrophes

Use an apostrophe in the possessive form of a noun (but not in a pronoun):

On *his* desk was a reply to Bette *Ainsley's* application for the *manager's* position.

Apostrophes are also used in place of the missing letter(s) of a contraction:

Whole Words	Contraction
we will	we'll
do not	don't
they are	they're

2.10 Quotation Marks

Use quotation marks to surround words that are repeated exactly as they were said or written:

The collection letter ended by saying, "This is your third and final notice."

Remember: (1) When the quoted material is a complete sentence, the first word is capitalized. (2) The final comma or period goes inside the closing quotation marks.

Quotation marks are also used to set off the title of a newspaper story, magazine article, or book chapter:

You should read "Legal Aspects of the Collection Letter" in *Today's Credit.*

The book title is shown here in italics. If italic font is not available, the title is underlined. The same treatment is proper for newspaper and magazine titles.

Quotation marks may also be used to indicate special treatment of words or phrases, such as terms that you're using in an unusual or ironic way:

Our management "team" spends more time squabbling than working to solve company problems.

When you are defining a word, put the definition in quotation marks:

The abbreviation *etc.* means "and so forth."

When using quotation marks, take care to insert the closing marks as well as the opening ones.

Although periods and commas go inside any quotation marks, colons and semicolons go outside them. A question mark goes inside the quotation marks only if the quotation is a question:

All that day we wondered, "Is he with us?"

If the quotation is not a question but the entire sentence is, the question mark goes outside:

What did she mean by "You will hear from me"?

2.11 Parentheses

Use parentheses to surround comments that are entirely incidental:

Our figures do not match yours, although (if my calculations are correct) they are closer than we thought.

Parentheses are also used in legal documents to surround figures in arabic numerals that follow the same amount in words:

Remittance will be One Thousand Two Hundred Dollars ($1200).

Be careful to put punctuation (period, comma, and so on) outside the parentheses unless it is part of the statement in parentheses.

2.12 Ellipses

Use ellipsis points, or dots, to indicate that material has been left out of a direct quotation. Use them only in direct quotations and only at the point where material was left out. In the following example, the first sentence is quoted in the second:

The Dow Jones Industrial Average, which skidded 38.17 points in the previous five sessions, gained 4.61 points to end at 2213.84.

According to the Montreal *Gazette,* "The Dow Jones Industrial Average . . . gained 4.61 points" on June 10.

The number of dots in ellipses is not optional; always use three. Occasionally, the points of ellipsis come at the end of a sentence, where they seem to grow a fourth dot. Don't be fooled: One of the dots is a period.

2.13 Underscores and Italics

Usually a line typed underneath a word or phrase either provides emphasis or indicates the title of a book, magazine, or newspaper. If possible, use italics instead of an underscore. Italics (or underlining) should also be used for defining terms and for discussing words as words:

In this report *net sales* refers to after-tax sales dollars.

The word *building* is a common noun and should not be capitalized.

Practice Session: Punctuation 2

Circle the letter of the preferred choice in each group of sentences. Answers to these exercises appear on page 172.

1. **a.** Capital One uses data mining to predict what customers might buy, and how the company can sell those products to them.

   b. Capital One uses data mining to predict what customers might buy and how the company can sell those products to them.

2. **a.** During the three-year lawsuit, pressure built to settle out of court.

   b. During the three-year lawsuit pressure built to settle out of court.

3. **a.** The music store, which had been in the Harper family for three generations, was finally sold to a conglomerate.

   b. The music store which had been in the Harper family for three generations was finally sold to a conglomerate.

4. **a.** After the fire, Hanson resolved to build a bigger better bottling plant.

   b. After the fire, Hanson resolved to build a bigger, better bottling plant.

5. **a.** Wild Oats, a chain of natural food grocery stores, uses kiosks to deliver nutrition information to customers.

   b. Wild Oats; a chain of natural food grocery stores; uses kiosks to deliver nutrition information to customers.

6. **a.** Management consultant Peter Drucker said "The aim of marketing is to know the customer so well that the product or service sells itself.

   b. Management consultant Peter Drucker said, "The aim of marketing is to know the customer so well that the product or service sells itself."

7. **a.** Companies use a wide variety of techniques - contests, displays, and giveaways, to name a few - to sell you things.

   b. Companies use a wide variety of techniques—contests, displays, and giveaways, to name a few—to sell you things.

   c. Companies use a wide variety of techniques—contests, displays, and giveaways to name a few—to sell you things.

8. **a.** Self-service outlets are becoming increasingly popular in a variety of retail situations.

   b. Self service outlets are becoming increasingly popular in a variety of retail situations.

   c. Selfservice outlets are becoming increasingly popular in a variety of retail situations.

9. **a.** Antiinflationary measures became a major priority for governments in the 1970s and 1980s.

  b. Anti-inflationary measures became a major priority for governments in the 1970s and 1980s.

10. **a.** The decision-making process depends on a buyer's culture, social class, and self-image.

  b. The decision-making process depends on a buyer's culture, social class, and self image.

  c. The decision making process depends on a buyer's culture, social class, and self-image.

11. **a.** Situation factors also play a role in consumer decision-making.

  b. Situation factors also play a role in consumer decision making.

12. **a.** Joel told me, "I can't stop humming this song in my head, 'There's a Moon Out Tonight."

  b. Joel told me, "I can't stop humming this song in my head, 'There's a Moon Out Tonight'."

  c. Joel told me, "I can't stop humming this song in my head, 'There's a Moon Out Tonight.'"

13. **a.** An insider at Arthur Andersen said that "the fall of the accounting giant stemmed from a series of poor management decisions made over decades."

  b. An insider at Arthur Andersen said that, "The fall of the accounting giant stemmed from a series of poor management decisions made over decades."

14. **a.** Have you read Jason Zein's article "Measuring the Internet?"

  b. Have you read Jason Zein's article "Measuring the Internet"?

15. **a.** According to Jamba Juice founder Kirk Peron, "jamba" is a West African word meaning *to celebrate.*

b. According to Jamba Juice founder Kirk Peron, *jamba* is a West African word meaning "to celebrate."

c. According to Jamba Juice founder Kirk Peron, "jamba" is a West African word meaning to celebrate.

Improve Your Grammar, Mechanics, and Usage

Level 1: Self-Assessment—Dashes and Hyphens

Review Sections 2.7 and 2.8, and then look at the following 15 items. Answers to Level 1 exercises appear on page 172.

In items 1–15, insert the required dashes (—) and hyphens (-):

1. Three qualities speed, accuracy, and reliability are desirable in any applicant to the data entry department.

2. A highly placed source explained the top secret negotiations.

3. The file on Maria Wilson yes, we finally found it reveals a history of late payments.

4. They're selling a well designed machine.

5. A bottle green sports jacket is hard to find.

6. Argentina, Brazil, Mexico these are the countries we hope to concentrate on.

7. Only two sites maybe three offer the things we need.

8. How many owner operators are in the industry?

9. Your ever faithful assistant deserves without a doubt, I'm sure a substantial raise.

10. Myrna Talefiero is this organization's president elect.

11. Stealth, secrecy, and surprise those are the elements that will give us a competitive edge.

12. The charts have been well placed on each page unlike the running heads and footers.

13. We got our small business loan an enormous advantage.

14. Ron Franklin do you remember him? will be in town Monday.

15. Your devil may care attitude affects everyone involved in the decision making process.

Level 2: Workplace Applications

The following items may contain errors in grammar, capitalization, punctuation, abbreviation, number style, and vocabulary. Rewrite each sentence in the space provided, correcting all errors. Write *C* in the space after any sentence that is already correct.

1. Commerce One helps its customer's to more efficiently lower administrative costs, improve order times, and to manage contract negotiations.

2. The multi-use bus vehicle seats up to 35 passengers, but is equipped with a 7 metre standardized container in the rear. The same container one sees on ships, trains and on planes.

3. A refusal to except the status quo has just created, in our opinion, Canada's newest and most exciting company to watch," said Gordon Exel, Vice-President Marketing of Westport Innovations.

4. This new, transportation model may have a global affect and the barriers to entry will be extremely costly too overcome.

5. Autobytel also owns and operates Carsmart.com and Autosite.com as well as AIC [Automotive Information Center] a provider of automotive marketing data and technology.

6. Mymarket.com offers a low cost high reward, entry into e-commerce not only for buyers but also suppliers.

7. One of Bombardier's main competitors in the manufacture of small aircraft are Brazilian-owned Embraer.

8. After identifying the factors that improve a industrial process, additional refining experiments must be conducted to confirm the results.

9. The employment standards Act regulates minimum wages, establishes overtime compensation, and it outlaws labour for children.

10. The Chinese government are supporting use of the Internet as a business tool because it is seen by it as necessary to enhance competitiveness.

11. At a certain point in a company's growth, the entrepreneur, who wants to control everything, can no longer keep up so they look mistakenly for a better manager and call that person a CEO.

12. City Fresh foods is paid by City health agencies to provide Ethnic food to the homebound "elderly" in the Vancouver Area.

13. Being in business since 2004, Ms Rosen has boiled down her life story into a 2-minute sound byte for sales prospects.

14. Anyone that wants to gain a new perspective on their product or service must cast aside one's own biases.

15. If I was the mayor, I'd handle local transportation issues much different.

Level 3: Document Critique

The following document may contain errors in grammar, capitalization, punctuation, abbreviation, number style, vocabulary, and spelling. You may also find problems with organization, format, and word use. Correct all errors using standard proofreading marks (see the Correction Symbols list on p. 179).

Memo

SUBJECT: Recruiting and hiring Seminar

To Jeff Black and HR staff

DATE March 14 2010

FROM: Carrie andrews

As you all know the process of recruiting screening and hiring new employees might be a legal minefield. Because we don't have an inhouse lawyer to help us make every decision, its important for all of us to be aware of what actions are legally acceptible and what isn't. Last week I attended a Canadian Federation of Independent Business workshop on this subject. I given enough useful information to warrant updating our online personnel handbook and perhaps developing a quick training session for all interviewing teams. First, heres a quick look at the things I learned.

Avoiding Legal Mistakes

- How to write recruiting ads that accurately portray job openings and not discriminate.
- Complying with the Canadian Human Rights Act and the Employment Equity Act
- How to use an employment agency effectively and safe (without risk of legal entanglements)

How to Screen and Interview More Effectively

- How to sort through résumés more efficient (including looking for telltale signs of false information)
- We can avoid interview questions that could violate applicant's rights

- When and how to check references'

Measuring Applicants

- Which type of preemployment tests have been proven most effective?
- Which language-related issues effect us

as you can see the seminar addressed alot of important information. We covering the basic guidelines for much of this already; but a number of specific recommendations and legal concepts should be emphisized and underline.

It will take me a couple of weeks to get the personel handbook updated: but we don't have any immediate hiring plans anyway so that shouldn't be too much of a problem unless you think I should complete it sooner and then we can talk about that.

I'll keep the seminar handouts and my notes on my desk in case you want to peruse them.

After the handbook is updated by me, we can get together and decide whether we need to train the interviewing team members.

Although we have a lot of new information, what people need to be aware of can be highlighted and the new sections can be read as schedules allow, although they might be reluctant to do this and we can also talk about that later, at a time of your conveinence that you can select later.

If you have any questions in the mean-time; don't hesitate to e-mail me or drop by for a chat.

Level 1: Self-Assessment—Quotation Marks, Parentheses, Ellipses, Underscores, and Italics

Review Sections 2.10, 2.11, 2.12, and 2.13, and then look at the following 15 items. Answers to Level 1 exercises appear on page 173.

In items 1–15, insert quotation marks, parentheses, ellipses, and underscores (for italics) wherever necessary:

1.   Be sure to read How to Sell by Listening in this month's issue of B.C. Business.

2.   Her response see the attached memo is disturbing.

3.   Contact is an overused word.

4.   We will operate with a skeleton staff during the holiday break December 21 through January 2.

5.   The SBP's next conference, the bulletin noted, will be held in Winnipeg.

6.   Sara O'Rourke the Edmonton Sun reporter who will be interviewing us will be here on Thursday.

7.   I don't care why you didn't fill my order; I want to know when you'll fill it.

8.   The term up in the air means undecided.

9.   Her assistant the one who just had the baby won't be back for four weeks.

10.   As soon as the journalist heard Prime Minister Trudeau begin a sentence with The state has no business in the bedrooms her jaw dropped.

11.   Whom do you think Time magazine will select as its Person of the Year?

12.   Do you remember who sang Fall to Pieces?

13. Refinements in robotics may prove profitable. More detail about this technology appears in Appendix A.

14. The resignation letter begins Since I'll never regain your respect and goes on to explain why that's true.

15. You must help her distinguish between i.e. which means that is and e.g. which means for example.

Level 2: Workplace Applications

The following items may contain errors in grammar, capitalization, punctuation, abbreviation, number style, and vocabulary. Rewrite each sentence in the space provided, correcting all errors. Write *C* in the space after any sentence that is already correct.

1. For the 1st time, thank's to largely deals with the big chains like Stop & Shop, Sheila's Snak Treetz are showing a profit.

2. Wireless devices—especially portable ones, changed our physical and cultural landscape more quick than people thought it would.

3. After moving into they're own factory, the Anderson's found theirselves in the market for an oven with airflow controls.

4. Cash-strapped entrepreneurs have learned penny-pinching, cost-cutting, credit-stretching techniques.

5. Designs in the Rough send out some 7 million catalogues a year yet until recently the company did'nt need a warehouse and they hadn't hardly any carrying costs.

6. We've hired a consultant to locate and interview people who live within a 15 minute drive of a Canadian Tire store.

124

124

7. Nestlé Waters North America are the exclusive importer of globally-recognized brands such as: Perrier and Vittel from France and, San Pelligrino from Italy.

8. The B.C. South Asian community; the second largest Minority Group in the province; commands impressive political power.

9. We conducted a six-month pilot in Halifax, to insure the affectiveness of the program.

10. A series of 7-Eleven television spots helped make the term brain freeze part of every day North American language.

11. The ad agencies accounts include the following consumer-brands; Wal-Mart, Westjet airlines, Kinko's, and Rocky Mountain Bicycles.

12. PETsMART allows pets and their humans to together stroll the aisles of its stores; the number one Specialty Retailer of pet supplies.

13. Signature Fruit Co. is expanding it's Ontario warehouses this Fall.

14. To unite the company's 91 franchisees around a common corporate identity WingsToGo have setup a corporate intranet.

15. It would be well for you to contract with an Internet service provider—a ISP - to both run and to maintain your Web site.

Level 3: Document Critique

The following document may contain errors in grammar, capitalization, punctuation, abbreviation, number style, vocabulary, and spelling. You may also find problems with organization, format, and word use. Correct all errors using standard proofreading marks (see the Correction Symbols list on p. 179).

Memorandum

From: Kris Beiersdorf

Date: 18 April 2009

RE PROJECT: Contract no. 05371 St. Cyril

To: Ken Estes, Drummondville concrete

Memco Construction is pleased to submit a road construction proposal for the above project. Our company has been providing quality materials and subcontracting services for highway reconstruction projects for over twenty-three years. Our most recent jobs in Quebec have included Highway Cap-de-la Madeleine resurfacing, and reconstructing Highway 1, St. Hyacinthe Bypass.

Should you have any questions about this proposal please contact me at the company 819-672-0344, direct extension #30) or by e-mail at kbeirsdorf@memcocon.com.

Based on the scope of the work outlined: the total cost of this job is projected by us to run ninety-nine thousand, two hundred eighty-three dollars. Because material quantities can vary once a project gets underway a separate page will be attached by us to this memorandum detailing our per-unit fees. Final charges will be based on the exact quantity of materials used for the job, and anything that accedes this estimate will be added of course.

Our proposal assumes that the following items will be furnished by other contractors (at no cost to Memco). All forms, earthwork and clearing; All prep work; Water at project site; Traffic control setup, devices, and maintenance—Location for staging, stockpiling, and storing material and equipment at job sight.

If we win this bid, we are already to begin when the apropriate contracts have been signed by us and by you.

3.0 Mechanics

The most obvious and least tolerable mistakes that a business writer makes are probably those related to grammar and punctuation. However, a number of small details, known as writing mechanics, demonstrate the writer's polish and reflect on the company's professionalism.

3.1 Capitals

Capitals are used at the beginning of certain word groups:

- **Complete sentence:**

  Before hanging up, he said, "We'll meet here on Wednesday at noon."

- **Formal statement following a colon:**

  She has a favourite motto: Where there's a will, there's a way.

  (Otherwise, the first word after a colon is not usually capitalized—see Section 2.5.)

- **Phrase used as sentence:**

  Absolutely not!

- **Quoted sentence embedded in another sentence:**

  Scot said, "Nobody was here during lunch hour except me."

- **List of items set off from text:**

  Three preliminary steps are involved:

      Design review

      Budgeting

      Scheduling

Capitalize proper adjectives and proper nouns (the names of particular persons, places, and things):

George Bowering lived in a Victorian mansion.

We sent Ms. Larson an application form, informing her that not all applicants are interviewed.

Let's consider opening a branch in the West, perhaps at the west end of Calgary, Alberta.

As office buildings go, the Kinney Building is a pleasant setting for TDG Office Equipment.

Although Ms. Larson's name is capitalized, the general term *applicants* is left uncapitalized. Likewise, *West* is capitalized when it refers to a particular place but not when it means a direction. In the same way, *office* and *building* are not capitalized when they are general terms (common nouns), but they are capitalized when they are part of the title of a particular office or building (proper nouns).

Titles within families, governments, or companies may also be capitalized:

I turned down Uncle David when he offered me a job, since I wouldn't be comfortable working for one of my relatives.

We've never had a president quite like President Sweeney.

People's titles are capitalized when they are used in addressing a person, especially in a formal context. They are not usually capitalized, however, when they are used merely to identify the person:

Address the letter to Chairperson Anna Palmer.

I wish to thank Chairperson Anna Palmer for her assistance.

Please deliver these documents to board chairperson Anna Palmer.

Anna Palmer, chairperson of the board, took the podium.

Also capitalize titles if they are used by themselves in addressing a person:

> Thank you, Doctor, for your donation.

Titles used to identify a person of very high rank are usually capitalized regardless of where they fall or how much of the name is included:

> the Prime Minister of Canada

> the Pope

In addresses, salutations, signature blocks, and some formal writing (such as acknowledgements), all titles are capitalized whether they come before or after the name. In addition, always capitalize the first word of the salutation and complimentary close of a letter:

> *Dear* Mr. Andrews: *Yours* very truly,

The names of organizations are capitalized, of course; so are the official names of their departments and divisions. However, do not use capitals when referring in general terms to a department or division, especially one in another organization:

> Route this memo to Personnel.

> Larry Tien was transferred to the Microchip Division.

> Will you be enrolled in the Psychology Department?

> Someone from the engineering department at EnerTech stopped by the booth.

> Our production department has reorganized for efficiency.

> Send a copy to their school of business administration.

Capitalization is unnecessary when using a word like *company, corporation,* or *university* alone:

> The corporation plans to issue 50 000 shares of common stock.

Likewise, the names of specific products are capitalized, although the names of general product types are not:

Dell computer   Tide laundry detergent

The names of languages, races, and ethnic groups are capitalized: *Japanese, Caucasian, Chinese.* But racial terms that denote only skin colour are usually not capitalized: *black, white.*

When referring to the titles of books, articles, magazines, newspapers, reports, movies, and so on, you should capitalize the first and last words and all nouns, pronouns, adjectives, verbs, adverbs, and prepositions and conjunctions with five letters or more. Except for the first and last words, do not capitalize articles:

Economics During the Great War

"An Investigation into the Market for Long-Distance Services"

"What Successes Are Made Of"

When *the* is part of the official name of a newspaper or magazine, it should be treated this way too: *The Globe and Mail.*

References to specific pages, paragraphs, lines, and the like are not capitalized: *page 73, line 3.* However, in most other numbered or lettered references, the identifying term is capitalized: *Chapter 4, Serial No. 382-2203, Item B-11.*

Finally, the names of academic degrees are capitalized when they follow a person's name but are not capitalized when used in a general sense:

I received a bachelor of science degree.

Thomas Chan, Doctor of Philosophy, will attend.

Similarly, general courses of study are not capitalized, but the names of specific classes are:

She studied accounting as an undergraduate.

She is enrolled in Accounting 201.

3.2 Abbreviations

Abbreviations are used heavily in tables, charts, lists, and forms. They're used sparingly in prose paragraphs, however. Here are some abbreviations often used in business writing:

Abbreviation	Full Term
b/l	bill of lading
ca.	circa (about)
dol., dols.	dollar, dollars
etc.	et cetera (and so on)
Inc.	Incorporated
L.f.	Ledger folio
Ltd.	Limited
mgr.	manager
NSF or N/S	not sufficient funds
P&L or P/L	profit and loss
reg.	regular
whsle.	wholesale

One way to handle an abbreviation that you want to use throughout a document is to spell it out the first time you use it, follow it with the abbreviation in parentheses, and then use the abbreviation in the remainder of the document.

Because *etc.* contains a word meaning "and," never write *and etc.* In fact, try to limit your use of such abbreviations to tables and parenthetical material.

3.3 Numbers

Numbers may be correctly handled many ways in business writing, so follow company style. In the absence of a set style, however, generally spell out all numbers from one to nine and use arabic numerals for the rest.

There are some exceptions to this general rule. For example, never begin a sentence with a numeral:

Twenty of us produced *641* units per week in the first *12* weeks of the year.

Use numerals for the numbers one through ten if they're in the same list as larger numbers:

Our weekly quota rose from *9* to *15* to *27*.

Use numerals for percentages, time of day (except with *o'clock*), dates, and (in general) dollar amounts.

Our division is responsible for *7* percent of total sales.

The meeting is scheduled for *8:30* a.m. on August *2*.

Add *$3* for postage and handling.

Use a space in numbers expressing thousands (*12 257*), unless your company specifies another style. In four-digit numbers the space is optional (*1257*). Use a comma in the accounting profession. When dealing with numbers in the millions and billions, combine words and figures: *7.3 million, 2 billion.*

When writing dollar amounts, use a decimal point only if cents are included. In lists of two or more dollar amounts, use the decimal point either for all or for none:

He sent two cheques, one for *$67.92* and one for *$90.00*.

When two numbers fall next to each other in a sentence, use figures for the number that is largest, most difficult to spell, or part of a physical measurement; use words for the other:

I have learned to manage a classroom of 30 twelve-year-olds.

She's won a bonus for selling 24 thirty-volume sets.

You'll need twenty 3-cm bolts.

In addresses, all street numbers except *One* are in figures. So are suite and room numbers and postal codes. For street names that are numbered, practice varies so widely that you should use the form specified on an organization's letterhead or in a reliable directory. All of the following examples are correct:

One Fifth Avenue	297 Ninth Street
1839 44th Street	11026 West 78 Place

Telephone numbers are always expressed in figures. Parentheses often separate the area code from the rest of the number, but a hyphen (or sometimes a slash or a dash) may be used instead, especially if the entire phone number is enclosed in parentheses:

382-8329   (602) 382-8329   (602-382-8329)   602-382-8329

Percentages are always expressed in figures. The word *percent* is used in most cases, but % may be used in tables, forms, and statistical writing.

Physical measurements such as distance, weight, and volume are also often expressed in figures: *9 km, 8.25 m, 4.7 kg.*

Ages are usually expressed in words—except when a parenthetical reference to age follows someone's name:

Mrs. Margaret Sanderson is seventy-two.

Mrs. Margaret Sanderson, 72, swims daily.

Also, ages expressed in years and months are treated like physical measurements that combine two units of measure: *5 years 6 months.*

Decimal numbers are always written in figures. In most cases, add a zero to the left of the decimal point if the number is less than one and does not already start with a zero:

    1.38   .07   0.2

In a series of related decimal numbers with at least one number greater than one, make sure that all numbers smaller than one have a zero to the left of the decimal point: *1.20, 0.21, 0.09.* Also, express all decimal numbers in a series to the same number of places by adding zeroes at the end:

    The responses were Yes, 37.2 percent; No, 51.0; Not Sure, 11.8.

Simple fractions are written in words, but more complicated fractions are expressed in figures or, if easier to read, in figures and words:

    two-thirds   9/32   2 hundredths

A combination of whole numbers and a fraction should always be written in figures. Note that a hyphen is used to separate the fraction from the whole number when a slash is used for the fraction: *2-11/16.*

3.4 Word Division

In general, avoid dividing words at the ends of lines. When you must do so, follow these rules:

- Don't divide one-syllable words (such as *since, walked,* and *thought*); abbreviations (*mgr.*); contractions (*isn't*); or numbers expressed in numerals (*117 500*).

- Divide words between syllables, as specified in a dictionary or word-division manual.

- Make sure that at least three letters of the divided word are moved to the second line: *sincerely* instead of *sincere-ly*.

- Do not end a page or more than three consecutive lines with hyphens.

- Leave syllables consisting of a single vowel at the end of the first line (*impedi-ment* instead of *imped-iment*), except when the single vowel is part of a suffix such as *-able, -ible, -ical,* or *-ity* (*re-spons-ible* instead of *re-sponsi-ble*).

- Divide between double letters (*tomor-row*), except when the root word ends in double letters (*call-ing* instead of *cal-ling*).

- Wherever possible, divide hyphenated words at the hyphen only: instead of *anti-inde-pendence,* use *anti-independence.*

Practice Session: Mechanics

Circle the letter of the preferred choice in each of the following groups of sentences. Answers to these exercises appear on page 174.

1. a. When you are in Vancouver for the Sales Meeting, be sure to visit the Marine Building.

    b. When you are in Vancouver for the sales meeting, be sure to visit the Marine building.

    c. When you are in Vancouver for the sales meeting, be sure to visit the Marine Building.

2. a. We plan to expand our national operations to the west, as well as the east.

    b. We plan to expand our national operations to the West, as well as the East.

    c. We plan to expand our national operations to the west, as well as the East.

3. a. Lee Marrs, who is President of Lee Marrs Designs, has been chosen to revamp our Web site.

    b. Lee Marrs, who is president of Lee Marrs Designs, has been chosen to revamp our Web site.

    c. Lee Marrs, who is president of Lee Marrs designs, has been chosen to revamp our Web site.

4. a. There's one thing we know for sure: Having a good idea doesn't guarantee success.

    b. There's one thing we know for sure: having a good idea doesn't guarantee success.

5. a. Be sure to order manila envelopes in all sizes: 9" x 12", 11", 14", etc.

b. Be sure to order manila envelopes in all sizes: 9" x 12", 11", 14", and etc.

6. **a.** The traditional trading period for Canadian stock exchanges is 9:30 a.m. to 4 o'clock p.m.

   b. The traditional trading period for Canadian stock exchanges is 9:30 a.m. to 4 p.m.

   c. The traditional trading period for Canadian stock exchanges is 9:30 a.m. to 4:00 p.m.

7. **a.** The number of members on the board of directors has been reduced from 13 to nine.

   b. The number of members on the board of directors has been reduced from 13 to 9.

8. **a.** The CDs are priced at $15, $12.95, and $11.00.

   b. The CDs are priced at $15.00, $12.95, and $11.00.

   c. The CDs are priced at $15, $12.95, and $11.

9. **a.** Twenty people have signed up for the spreadsheet software class, but there is room for 25.

   b. 20 people have signed up for the spreadsheet software class, but there is room for 25.

10. **a.** The best way to divide the word *sincerely* is "sin-cerely."

    b. The best way to divide the word *sincerely* is "sincere-ly."

Improve Your Grammar, Mechanics, and Usage

Level 1: Self-Assessment—Capitals and Abbreviations

Review Sections 3.1 and 3.2, and then look at the following 15 items. Answers to Level 1 exercises appear on page 175.

In items 1–15, indicate proper capitalization by underlining appropriate letters. Circle abbreviations that should be spelled out, and insert abbreviations where appropriate.

136

1. Dr. paul singha is joining our staff.

2. New caressa skin cream should be in a position to dominate that market.

3. Send this report to mister h. k. danforth, p.o. box 2243, riley, ab T5S 4S2.

4. You are responsible for training my new assistant to operate the xerox machine.

5. She received her m.b.a. from the university of New Brunswick.

6. The building is located on Champlain street near Alcan place.

7. Call me early in the a.m., and I'll have the information you need.

8. When jones becomes ceo next month, we'll need your input.

9. Address it to head of production art bowers.

10. Please rsvp to sony corp. just as soon as you know your schedule.

11. The data-processing department will begin work on feb. 2, just one wk. from today.

12. You are to meet her on friday in her office at the economics dept.

13. Whenever you can come, professor, our employees will greatly enjoy your presentation.

14. At 50 per box, our std. contract forms are $9.00 a box, and our warranty forms are $7.95 a box.

15. We plan to establish a sales office on the west coast.

Level 2: Workplace Applications

The following items may contain errors in grammar, capitalization, punctuation, abbreviation, number style, and vocabulary. Rewrite each sentence in the space provided, correcting all errors. Write *C* in the space after any sentence that is already correct.

1. The Demographer David Foot, uses population data cleverly. To explain Canadian social trends and to make long term economic predictions.

2. Louis Vuitton, the internationally-renowned luggage maker and specialty retailer plan to open a 1000 square metre store in Edmonton, AB next year.

3. If none of the solutions seem satisfying, pick the more easier one.

4. Ken Baker, the west coast bureau chief for Macleans magazine, will be responsible for overseeing all of magazine reporting in Vancouver, conducting high profile, celebrity interviews, for identifying news stories, and assist in the generation of cover concepts.

5. With experience managing numerous enthusiast brands, including "Kawasaki" and "Skechers," Juxt Interactive are cementing their role as a leader in strategic, integrated campaigns.

6. You're message, tone, and product positioning has to be right on to be excepted and successful.

7. As I begun to put the team together, it became apparent to myself that my idea was ahead of it's time.

8. Many think that the primary market for newspapers are the readers, however advertisers generate the majority of revenues.

9. MECs new Web site, www.MEC.com, features items that are not available at MEC's physical stores, catalogue, or main website.

10. The company's C.E.O., who we had saw at the awards dinner wednesday night, was fired the next day.

11. A designer of high priced purses such as Kate Spade or Louis Vuitton generally limit distribution to exclusive boutiques or high end retail stores: such as Holt Renfrew.

12. There is many indications that an economic recovery is underway, and will continue to stabilize and build however modestly.

13. We bought the equipment at a second hand store which turned out to be shoddy and defective.

14. Experts site 2 principle reasons for Webvan's failure; consumer resistance and over expansion.

15. Implementation of the over time hours guidelines will be carried out by the Human Resources Staff members.

Level 3: Document Critique

The following document may contain errors in grammar, capitalization, punctuation, abbreviation, number style, vocabulary, and spelling. You may also find problems with organization, format, and word use. Correct all errors using standard proofreading marks (see the Correction Symbols list on p. 179).

Date: Thu, 25 April, 2010

From: Steve Pendergrass

To: Gregory Hansford

CC:

BCC:

Attached:

Subject: Library Hours

Dear Mr. Hansford,

There is a favourite place in which Northern Alberta Institute of Technology students study on our campus: the library because of the quiet atmosphere excellent resources, and helpful staff. With a ajustment in library hours there assets could be taken advantage of by more students.

In an informal survey of the students in my English class, a desire for the library to be open more hours on the weekends became evident. Many students find weekends best for researching term papers: because that's when large blocks of time can be found in their schedules.

I'd like to sight several reasons for the change I am about to propose to encourage your interest and desire for my suggestion. Understandable, librarians need a day off. Perhaps students and librarians could both be accomodated if the library closed at five p.m. on Friday night. Friday night is the time most students like to relax and attend sports events or parties. The libary could then be open on Saturdays from ten a.m. until 4:30 p.m. To make this arrangement fair to librarians; perhaps their schedules could be staggered so that nobody would have to work every Saturday or those scheduled to work on Saturdays could be given Mondays or Fridays off.

Consider implementing this new schedule this Fall. Another much-appreciated service for students will be performed if you do this.

Sincerely: Steve Pendergrass, student

Level 1: Self-Assessment—Numbers

Review Section 3.3 and then look at the following 15 items. Answers to Level 1 exercises appear on page 175.

For items 1–15, correct the number style wherever necessary:

1. We need to hire one office manager, four bookkeepers, and twelve assistants.

2. The market for this product is nearly six million people in our region alone.

3. Make sure that all 1835 pages are on my desk no later than nine o'clock a.m.

4. 2008 was the year that Jasminder Bohal sold more than $50 thousand dollars worth of stock.

5. Our deadline is 2010/09/22, but we won't be ready before 2011/02/22.

6.   95 percent of our customers are men.

7.   More than 1/2 the Canadian population is female.

8.   Cecile Simmons, thirty-eight, is the first woman in this company to be promoted to management.

9.   Last year, I wrote 20 15-page reports, and Michelle wrote 24 three-page reports.

10.   Of the 15 applicants, seven are qualified.

11.   Our blinds should measure 90 cm wide by one and one-half metres long by 4 cm deep.

12.   Deliver the couch to seven eighty-three Fountain Rd., Suite three, Drayton Valley, AB, TYN 5H5.

13.   Here are the corrected figures: 42.7% agree, 23.25% disagree, 34% are undecided, and the error is .05%.

14.   You have to agree that 5 000 000 Canadian citizens cannot be wrong.

15.   We need a set of shelves 1 point two five metres long.

Level 2: Workplace Applications

The following items may contain errors in grammar, capitalization, punctuation, abbreviation, number style, and vocabulary. Rewrite each sentence in the space provided, correcting all errors. Write *C* in the space after any sentence that is already correct.

1.   Speaking at a recent software conference Alan Nichols; ceo of Tekco Systems; said the companys' goal is to reduce response time to 2 to 4 hrs., using software as an enabler.

2.   Selling stocks short are the latest rage on wall street, where lately things have just gone from bad to worst.

3. As Electronic Commerce grows people are trying to find new ways to make money off of it.

4. We give a notification not only to the customer but also our salespeople that the product has been shipped because they will want to follow up.

5. When deciding between these various suppliers, we found that each of them offer both advantages and also disadvantages.

6. I found the book, "Marketing is Easy, Selling is Hard," for three different prices on the Internet: $14, $13.25, and $12.00.

7. United Agra Products, a distributor of fertilizers and seeds, in transmission of customer orders over it's private network faced the possibility of serious bottlenecks.

8. The answers you receive on your questionnaire, are influenced by the types of question you ask, the way they are asked, and your subjects cultural and language background.

9. The creation of hazardous by products, like silver in film processing, require us to collect our used chemicals for disposal at a hazardous-waste-facility.

10. As a source of ingredients for our products, we try to establish relationships with small cooperative or farming communities - often in developing countries – because, we believe that the best way to improve peoples' lives is to give them a chance at self reliance.

11. A entrepreneur really should never be in any organization that get's so big that it looses intimacy.

12. Racecar Driver Eddie Cheever, is founder of Aleanza Marketing Group, a seven-person company that handles $10 million dollars in sponsorship campaigns for Cheevers' team Red Bull Cheever Racing.

13. Over the last six years, Business Cluster Development have started 13 technology related incubators, that they call 'business clusters.'

14. In an interview, Gary Hoover said "When I dreamed up Bookstop, we asked people, "If there was a bookstore that carried a huge selection of books and had them all at discount prices, would you go there"? and we got a lot of yawns".

15. The chief attraction of vending machines are their convenience, they are open 24 hours a day, on the other hand, vending machine prices are no bargain.

Level 3: Document Critique

The following document may contain errors in grammar, capitalization, punctuation, abbreviation, number style, vocabulary, and spelling. You may also find problems with word use and format. Correct all errors using standard proofreading marks (see the Correction Symbols list on p. 179).

The Executve Summary (Excerpt)

Purpose of the Proposal

This document will acquaint the reader with 3 principle topics by

- Showing what the Queen's Solar Vehicle Team is (QSVT)

- Showing that the team-oriented, inerdepartmental diciplines at Queen's University possesses the tenacity and knowhow to repeat they're previous successes with a solar-powered vehical in the World solar Challenge Race in Austrailia in 2009;

- Define and articulate how this business team expect to promote and generate the neccesary support; funds, and materials from the student body, alumni, community and local businesses to sieze and executive this opportunity;

Project Profile

The QSVT project raced it's first Solar Car in Summer of 1988 when a group of Queen's university mechanical engineering students inspired by the Great Canadian Solar Challenge, committed itself to designing and building a superior solar-powered vehicle (called Photomoto). Other Queens vehicles: Radiance, Gemini, and, our 10th Solar Car, Ultraviolet, have won many awards and placed first or second in numerous international races. Including Sunrayce, the American Solar Challenge, adn the World Solar Challenge.

From the Beginning, the QSVT project quickly revolved into a cross-disciplinary educational effort encompassing students from many departments of Queen's Univ. The project has provides students participants and volunteers with valuable real life experiences and has brought them together in an effort that benefits not only the students and the university but also the environment.

Sponsors of this project are not only contributing to the successful achievment of the overall QSVT project but will also enhance their goodwill, advertising, and name promotion by association with the project. In addition, the project offers a unique opportunity for the companies who can donate parts and accessories to showcase their name and test field their products in public in this highly publicized international contest.

4.0 Vocabulary

Using the right word in the right place is a crucial skill in business communication. However, many pitfalls await the unwary.

4.1 Frequently Confused Words

Because the following sets of words sound similar, be careful not to use one when you mean to use the other:

Word	Meaning
accede	to comply with
exceed	to go beyond
accept	to take
except	to exclude
access	admittance
excess	too much
advice	suggestion
advise	to suggest
affect	to influence
effect	the result
allot	to distribute
a lot	much or many
all ready	completely prepared
already	completed earlier
born	having been given birth
borne	carried
capital	money; chief city

capitol	a government building (U.S.)
cite	to quote
sight	a view
site	a location
complement	the complete amount; to go well with
compliment	expression of esteem; to flatter
co-respondent	party in a divorce suit
correspondent	letter writer
council	a panel of people
counsel	advice; a lawyer
defer	to put off until later
differ	to be different
device	a mechanism
devise	to plan
die	to stop living; a stamping tool; one of a pair of dice
dye	to colour
discreet	careful
discrete	separate
envelop	to surround
envelope	a covering for a letter
forth	forward
fourth	number four in a sequence
holey	full of holes
holy	sacred
wholly	completely

human	pertaining to human beings
humane	kindly
incidence	a statistical rate
incidents	events
instance	example
instants	moments
interprovincial	between provinces
intraprovincial	within a province
later	afterwards
latter	the second of two
lead	a metal; to guide
led	guided
lean	to rest at an angle
lien	a claim
levee	embankment
levy	tax
loath	reluctant
loathe	to hate
loose	free; not tight
lose	to mislay
material	substance
materiel	equipment
miner	mineworker
minor	underage person
moral	virtuous; a lesson

morale	sense of well-being
ordinance	law
ordnance	weapons
overdo	to do in excess
overdue	past due
peace	lack of conflict
piece	a fragment
pedal	a foot lever; to push a foot lever
peddle	to sell
persecute	to torment
prosecute	to bring to justice
personal	private
personnel	employees
precedence	priority
precedents	previous events; previous cases used as examples
principal	sum of money; chief; main
principle	general rule
rap	to knock
wrap	to cover
residence	home
residents	inhabitants
right	correct
rite	ceremony
write	to set down words
role	a part to play

roll	to tumble; a list
root	part of a plant
route	a traveller's way
rout	to defeat
shear	to cut
sheer	thin, steep
stationary	immovable
stationery	paper
than	as compared with
then	at that time
their	belonging to them
there	in that place
they're	they are
to	a preposition
too	excessively; also
two	the number
waive	to set aside
wave	a swell of water; a gesture
weather	atmospheric conditions
whether	if
who's	contraction of "who is" or "who has"
whose	possessive form of "who"

In the preceding list, only enough of each word's meaning is given to help you distinguish between the words in each group. Several meanings are left out entirely. For more complete definitions, consult a dictionary.

Practice Session: Confused Words

In the following sentences, underline the preferred choice within each set of parentheses. Answers to these exercises appear on page 176.

1.   If our bid is (*accepted, excepted*), we will begin the project in November.

2.   This Web site offers some great (*advice, advise*) on setting up a new business.

3.   How will the accounting scandal (*affect, effect*) that corporation's future?

4.   Most of the costs of the project will be (*born, borne*) by the contractor.

5.   In preparing the budget, we have to decide where best to invest our (*capital, capitol*).

6.   Be sure to (*cite, site*) the sources for your data when you prepare your report.

7.   The acquisition of LPC Group should (*compliment/complement*) our other holdings.

8.   Leo sought the (*council, counsel*) of his attorney before signing the contract.

9.   I didn't have to be told to be (*discrete, discreet*) about the sexual harassment case.

10.   When Jennings Hardware got behind in its debts, one of the creditors placed a (*lean, lien*) on its building.

11.   Mr. Hathaway was (*loath, loathe*) to fire Elizabeth, but he had no choice.

12.   To comply with local zoning (*ordinances, ordnances*), we had to replace our sign.

13.   As a teenager, Gary Sassaman used to (*pedal, peddle*) newspapers in downtown Halifax.

14.   Business owners along Yonge Street have vowed to (*persecute, prosecute*) anyone caught painting graffiti on their buildings.

15. We don't know of any (*precedence, precedents*) for the exponential growth of sales for this kind of product.

16. The (*principle, principal*) reason for closing down operations was obsolete production equipment that was too expensive to replace.

17. It's hard to say what (*role, roll*) the downturn in the economy played in the failure of Seven Hills Distribution.

18. Sunbeam employees were shocked by new CEO Al Dunlap's (*shear, sheer*) ruthlessness in axing jobs and slashing costs.

19. Now that our area code has changed, we will need to order new (*stationary, stationery*).

20. The Li brothers couldn't decide (*weather, whether*) to form a partnership or establish a corporation.

4.2 Frequently Misused Words

The following words tend to be misused for reasons other than their sound. Reference books (including the *Canadian Oxford Dictionary,* Partridge's *Usage & Abusage,* and Fowler's *Modern English Usage*) can help you with similar questions of usage.

a lot: When the writer means "many," *a lot* is always two separate words, never one.

correspond with: Use this phrase when you are talking about exchanging letters. Use *correspond to* when you mean "to be similar to" or "to be equivalent to." Use either *correspond with* or *correspond to* when you mean "to relate to" or "to agree with," when speaking of ideas or other abstract things.

disinterested: This word means "fair, unbiased, having no favourites, impartial." If you mean "bored" or "not interested," use *uninterested.*

etc.: This abbreviated form of the Latin phrase *et cetera* means "and so on" or "and so forth." The current tendency among business writers is to use the English phrase.

imply/infer: Both refer to hints. Their great difference lies in who is acting. The writer implies, or suggests; the reader infers, or reads between the lines.

lay: This word is a transitive verb. Never use it for the intransitive *lie.* (See Section 1.3.3.)

less: Use *less* for uncountable quantities (such as amounts of water, air, sugar, and oil). Use *fewer* for countable quantities (such as numbers of jars, saws, words, pages, and humans). The same distinction applies to *much* and *little* (uncountable) versus *many* and *few* (countable).

like: Use *like* only when the word that follows is just a noun or a pronoun. Use *as* or *as if* when a phrase or clause follows:

She looks like him.

She did just as he had expected.

It seems as if she had plenty of time.

many/much: See *less.*

regardless: The *less* ending is the negative part. No word needs two negative parts, so don't add *ir* (a negative prefix) to the beginning. There is no such word as *irregardless.*

to me/personally: Use these phrases only when personal reactions, apart from company policy, are being stated (not often the case in business writing).

try: Always follow with *to,* never *and.*

verbal: People in the business community who are careful with language frown on those who use *verbal* to mean "spoken" or "oral." Many others do say "verbal agreement." Strictly speaking, *verbal* means "of words" and therefore includes both spoken and written words. Follow company usage in this matter.

Practice Session: Misused Words

In the following sentences, underline the preferred choice within each set of parentheses. Answers to these exercises appear on page 177.

1. My boss told me that I still have (*a lot, alot*) to learn.

2. The Canadian Parliament corresponds (*to, with*) the British Parliament.

3. I tried to convince my co-workers to sign up for the stress-reduction program, but they all seemed (*uninterested, disinterested*).

4. When you say that the books have some discrepancies, are you (*inferring, implying*) that our accountant is embezzling from us?

5. From the auditor's silent stare, Margaret (*implied, inferred*) that the man was not amused by her jokes.

6. The report came out to (*less, fewer*) pages than we had originally anticipated.

7. Mr. Martens was treating Heather (*like, as if*) she had done something wrong.

8. You have to finish the job, (*irregardless, regardless*) of your loathing for it.

9. When talking to customers on the phone, try (*and, to*) be as pleasant as possible.

10. When making (*an oral, a verbal*) presentation, it's a good idea to make eye contact with your audience.

4.3 Frequently Misspelled Words

All of us, even the world's best spellers, sometimes have to check a dictionary for the spelling of some words. People who have never memorized the spelling of commonly used words must look up so many that they grow exasperated and give up on spelling words correctly.

Don't expect perfection, and don't surrender. If you can memorize the spelling of just the words listed here, you'll need the dictionary far less often, and you'll write with more confidence.

absence	bankruptcy	consensus
absorption	believable	convenient
accessible	brilliant	convertible
accommodate	bulletin	corroborate
accumulate	calendar	criticism
achieve	campaign	definitely
advantageous	category	description
affiliated	ceiling	desirable
aggressive	changeable	dilemma
alignment	clientele	disappear
apparent	collateral	disappoint
appropriate	committee	disbursement
argument	comparative	discrepancy
asphalt	competitor	dissatisfied
assistant	concede	dissipate
asterisk	congratulations	eligible
auditor	connoisseur	embarrassing

endorsement	intermediary	persistent
exaggerate	irresistible	personnel
exceed	judicial	persuade
exhaust	legitimate	possesses
existence	leisure	precede
extraordinary	licence/license	predictable
fallacy	litigation	preferred
familiar	maintenance	privilege
flexible	mathematics	procedure
fluctuation	mediocre	proceed
forty	minimum	pronunciation
gesture	necessary	psychology
grievous	negligence	pursue
haphazard	negotiable	questionnaire
harassment	newsstand	receive
holiday	noticeable	recommend
illegible	occurrence	repetition
immigrant	omission	rescind
incidentally	parallel	rhythmical
indelible	pastime	ridiculous
independent	peaceable	saleable
indispensable	permanent	secretary
insistent	perseverance	seize

separate	surprise	unanimous
sincerely	tangible	until
succeed	tariff	vacillate
suddenness	technique	vacuum
superintendent	tenant	vicious
supersede	truly	

Practice Session: Misspelled Words

In the following sentences, underline the preferred choice within each set of parentheses. Answers to these exercises appear on page 177.

1. We try to (*accomodate, accommodate*) any reasonable request from our customers.

2. Our preferred (*clientelle, clientele*) program has increased customer loyalty by nearly 10 percent.

3. Because the weather in St. John's is so (*changable, changeable*), the conference reception has a backup indoor venue.

4. The board reached a (*concensus, consensus*) on the new CEO.

5. It will be (*embarassing, embarrassing*) for the company if this information leaks out.

6. The auditors discovered the (*existance, existence*) of hidden accounts in foreign banks.

7. Every company should have a written sexual (*harassment, harrassment*) policy.

8. In today's book business, (*independant, independent*) publishers are having a tough time finding distribution.

9. This gadget was developed for office use, but it has actually made us more money as a (*leisure, liesure*) product.

10. The cost of any potentially (*neccessary, necessary*) adjustments will be borne by the vendor.

11. With all the turmoil (*occuring, occurring*) in the stock market, we've decided to shift our investments toward real estate.

12. The marketing survey found that consumers (*prefered, preferred*) brand-name dog food over generic brands.

13. Because her cost-cutting measures saved the company millions of dollars, Carolyn Kelly (*received, recieved*) a raise and a promotion.

14. Please send (*separate, seperate*) invoices for the two projects.

15. My supervisor didn't need to be so (*vicious, viscious*) in his critique of my performance.

158

4.4 Transitional Words and Phrases

The following sentences don't communicate as well as they might because they lack a transitional word or phrase:

> Production delays are inevitable. Our current lag time in filling orders is one month.

A semicolon between the two sentences would signal a close relationship between their meanings, but it wouldn't even hint at what that relationship is. Here are the sentences again, now linked by means of a semicolon, with a space for a transitional word or phrase:

> Production delays are inevitable; _____, our current lag time in filling orders is one month.

Now read the sentence with *nevertheless* in the blank space. Now try *therefore, incidentally, in fact,* and *at any rate* in the blank. Each substitution changes the meaning of the sentence.

Here are some transitional words (called conjunctive adverbs) that will help you write more clearly:

accordingly	furthermore	moreover
anyway	however	otherwise
besides	incidentally	still
consequently	likewise	therefore
finally	meanwhile	

The following transitional phrases are used in the same way:

as a result	in other words
at any rate	in the second place
for example	on the other hand
in fact	to the contrary

When one of these words or phrases joins two independent clauses, it should be preceded by a semicolon and followed by a comma, as shown here:

> The consultant recommended a complete reorganization; moreover, she suggested that we drop several products.

Improve Your Grammar, Mechanics, and Usage

Level 1: Self-Assessment—Vocabulary

Review Sections 4.1, 4.2, and 4.3, and then look at the following 15 items. Answers to these exercises appear on page 177.

In items 1–7, write the correct word in the space provided:

1. Everyone (*accept/except*) _____ Barbara King has registered for the company competition.

2. We need to find a new security (*device/devise*) _____.

3. The Hamiltons are (*loath/loathe*) _____ to admit that they are wrong.

4. The judge has ruled that this town cannot enforce such a local (*ordinance/ordnance*) _____.

5. To stay on schedule, we must give (*precedence/precedents*) _____ to the Marley project.

6. This month's balance is greater (*than/then*) _____ last month's.

7. That decision lies with the director, (*who's/whose*) _____ in charge of this department.

In items 8–15, underline errors and write corrections in the space provided:

8. _____ In this department, we see alot of mistakes like that.

9. _____ Three more elegible candidates are waiting to be interviewed.

10. _____ He decided to reveal the information, irregardless of the consequences.

11. _____ Why not go along when it is so easy to accomodate his demands?

12. _____ When you say that, do you mean to infer that I'm being unfair?

13. _____ She says that she finds this sort of ceremony embarassing.

14. _____ All we have to do is try and get along with him for a few more days.

15. _____ A friendly handshake should always preceed negotiations.

Level 2: Workplace Applications

The following items may contain errors in grammar, capitalization, punctuation, abbreviation, number style, and vocabulary. Rewrite each sentence in the space provided, correcting all errors. Write *C* in the space after any sentence that is already correct.

1. An entrepreneur and their business, are so closely tied together that a bank will want to see how they handle their personal affairs, before granting a small business line of credit.

2. The companys' annual meeting will be held from 2-4 PM. on May 3d in the Grand room at the Delta hotel.

3. Hundreds of outstanding students from coast-to-coast, have realized their dreams of a college or university education thanks to union-funded scholarship programs.

4. If you're home is you're principle place of business you can deduct generally the cost of travelling from you're home, to any business destination.

5. Companies like Fido sprung into being in the 1990's to provide mobile phone services to small- and medium-size businesses in competition with the established telecoms.

6. Some question whether a 'new economy' exists and if so how it differs from the old economy?

7. When the music industry claimed by stealing intellectual property Napster were committing piracy - Napster argued that it was'nt doing anything illegal or un-ethical.

8. The World Bank plays an important roll in todays fast changing closely-meshed global economy.

9. When it comes to consumer rights Health Canada, Agriculture Canada and local health departments are concerned not only with safety but also accurate information.

10. Fujitsu, a $50 billion company with 190 000 employees, dominates the Japanese computer industry.

11. The fortune 500 ranks not only corporations by size but also offers brief company descriptions; along with industry statistics, and additional measures of corporate performance.

12. Having bought 55 companies over the past decade, plans to make ten to 15 new acquisitions each year are being made by Cisco Systems.

13. In 1984 Michael Dell decided to sell P.C.'s direct and built to order, now everybody in the industry are trying to imitate Dells' strategy.

14. Resulting in large cost savings for the company, American Express have reduced the number of field office's from 85 to 7 by using virtual teams.

15. The third generation of mobile phones let people send text messages to other users; exchange e-mail; read the morning news; surfing certain Web sites; and to make purchases such as movie tickets and charge it to they're monthly phone bill.

Level 3: Document Critique

The following document may contain errors in grammar, capitalization, punctuation, abbreviation, number style, vocabulary, and spelling. Based on what you've learned in this chapter, you may also find problems with organization, usage, and word choice. Correct all errors using standard proofreading marks (see the Correction Symbols list on p. 179).

MORGAN McLeod

2397 Glencrest ridge, Ottawa, ON K1K 4R3

(613) 226-1804

February 2 2010:

Norton Acctg. Group

Ms Nan Hamadi, Human Resources

3778 Parkway North

Ottawa, ON K1K 5P8

Dear Ms. Hamadi—

With your companys' reputation for quality, customer service, employee empowerment, you'll will want to hire someone who is not only accurrate and efficient but also self motivated and results-oriented—someone who is able to make decisions as well as coperate with team members and clients. The ad you placed in the February 1st issue of *The National Post* for someone to fill a financial management position really has me very excited and eager.

During my 3 years at EnCana corporation -see attached resume- I've conducted internal auditing for accounts valued at $450 million dollars. Some of my many, countless accomplishments include

■   Increasing both internal and client support for the auditing process

■   I save the company over 2.5 million dollars when I discovered billing errors

■   Suggest ways accounts receivable processes could be streamlined

In addition it might be that Norton Accounting may appreciate my ability to complete projects on time as well as keeping them under budget. One of my priorities is a position in which my expereince will be broaden: so any opportunity to travel would be welcomed by me!

I'll be in your area during the weak of February 20; I'll call your office on Feb. 8 to see whether we can arrange to meet. I hope you'll give me a chance, please.

Sincerely,

Morgan McLeod,

Applicant

Answer Key

Diagnostic Test of English Skills

1.	E	16.	E	31.	B	46.	A
2.	D	17.	D	32.	A	47.	A
3.	E	18.	C	33.	A	48.	E
4.	C	19.	A	34.	B	49.	B
5.	E	20.	E	35.	B	50.	E
6.	A			36.	B		
7.	E	21.	A	37.	B	51.	A
8.	B	22.	B	38.	A	52.	A
9.	D	23.	B	39.	B	53.	B
10.	C	24.	A	40.	A	54.	A
		25.	B			55.	A
11.	C	26.	B	41.	D	56.	B
12.	B	27.	A	42.	B	57.	A
13.	A	28.	B	43.	D	58.	B
14.	D	29.	B	44.	D	59.	B
15.	B	30.	A	45.	E	60.	A

1.1 Nouns

Practice Session

1.	City	9.	company's
2.	Building / building	10.	editor-in-chief's
3.	hotels	11.	businesses'
4.	*t*'s / *i*'s	12.	passengers'
5.	1990s	13.	day's
6.	shelves	14.	Dallas's
7.	specialties	15.	Jones's
8.	cases		

Level 1: Self-Assessment: Nouns

1. Give the <u>balance sheet</u> to Melissa. (1.1.1)

2. We'd like to order 50 more <u>cases</u> for Craigmont Stores, and <u>3</u> each for the other <u>stores</u> on our <u>list</u>. (1.1.1)

3. Tarnower Corporation donates a portion of its profits to charity every year. (1.1.1)

4. Which aluminum bolts are packaged? (1.1.1)

5. Please send the Joneses a dozen of the following: stopwatches, canteens, headbands, and wristbands. (1.1.1)

6. The technician has already repaired the machine for the client. (1.1.2)

7. An attorney will talk to the group about incorporation. (1.1.2)

8. After her vacation, the buyer prepared a third-quarter budget. (1.1.2)

9. The new flat monitors are serving our department very well. (1.1.2)

10. Accuracy overrides speed in importance. (1.1.2)

11. copies   Make sure that all copys include the new addresses. (1.1.2)

12. employees'   Ask Jennings to collect all employee's donations for the United Way drive. (1.1.4)

13. sons-in-law/businesses   Charlie now has two son-in-laws to help him with his two online business's. (1.1.3, 1.1.4)

14. parentheses   Avoid using too many parenthesises when writing your reports. (1.1.3)

15. Burgess's/week's   Follow President Burgesses rules about what makes up a weeks work. (1.1.4)

1.2 Pronouns: Practice Session

1.	me	6.	its	11.	her	16.	your
2.	she	7.	his or her	12.	him or her	17.	its
3.	him	8.	Who	13.	her	18.	I
4.	We	9.	whom	14.	its	19.	their
5.	me	10.	Whom	15.	Who	20.	its

Level 1: Self-Assessment: Pronouns

1. whom   To which retailer will you send your merchandise? (1.2)

2. them   Have you given John and Nancy a list of parts? (1.2)

3. It/them   The main office sent the invoice to Mr. and Mrs. Litvak on December 5. (1.2)

4. its   The company settled the company's accounts before the end of the year (1.2)

5. Whose   Which person's umbrella is this? (1.2)

6.   The sales staff is preparing guidelines for its *(their, its)* clients. (1.2.5)

7.   Few of the sales representatives turn in their *(their, its)* reports on time. (1.2.5)

8.   The board of directors has chosen its *(their, its)* officers. (1.2.5)

9.   Donna and Eileen have told their *(her, their)* clients about the new program. (1.2.1)

10.   Each manager plans to expand his or her *(his, their, his or her)* sphere of control next year. (1.2.3)

11.   Has everyone supplied his or her *(his, their, his or her)* social insurance number? (1.2.3)

12.   After giving every employee a *(his, their, a)* raise, George told them *(them, they, all)* about the increased workload. (1.2.3, 1.2.4)

13.   Bob and Tim have opposite ideas about how to achieve company goals. Who *(Who, Whom)* do you think will win the debate? (1.2.4)

14.   City Securities has just announced whom *(who, whom)* it will hire as CEO. (1.2.4)

15.   Either of the new products would readily find its *(their, its)* place in the marketplace. (1.2.5)

1.3: Verbs

Practice Session

1.	comes, want	6.	sits	11.	is	16.	is
2.	knew	7.	set	12.	are	17.	are
3.	begun	8.	raise	13.	is	18.	is
4.	lie	9.	was	14.	is	19.	send
5.	laid	10.	is	15.	represents	20.	were

Level 1: Self-Assessment: Verbs

1.   have become (1.3.1)

2.   knew (1.3.1)

3.   had chosen (1.3.1)

4.   will do (1.3.1)

5.   will have returned (1.3.1)

6.   Leslie Cartwright will write the report. (1.3.5)

7.   I did not record the transaction. (1.3.5)

8.   Has the claims department notified you of your rights? (1.3.5)

9.   Our firm uses their services for hardware upgrades. (1.3.5)

10.   The customer returned the damaged equipment before we even located a repair facility. (1.3.5)

11.   Everyone upstairs (*receive*/ *receives*) mail before we do. (1.3.4)

12.   Neither the main office nor the branches (*is*/ *are*) blameless. (1.3.4)

13.   C&B Sales (*is* /*are*) listed in the directory. (1.3.4)

14.   When measuring shelves, 10 cm (*is* /*are*) significant. (1.3.4)

15.   About 90 percent of the employees (*plan* /*plans*) to come to the company picnic. (1.3.4)

1.4: Adjectives

Level 1: Self-Assessment—Adjectives

1.   greater (1.4.1)

2.   perfect (1.4.1)

3.   most interesting (1.4.1)

4.   better (1.4.1)

5.   hardest (1.4.1)

6.   A highly placed source revealed Dotson's last-ditch efforts to cover up the mistake. (1.4.2)

7.   Please send an extra-large dust cover for my photocopier. (1.4.2)

8.   A top-secret document was taken from the president's office last night. (1.4.2)

9.   A 30-year-old person should know better. (1.4.2)

10. If I write a large-scale report, I want to know that it will be read by upper-level management. (1.4.2)

11. The two companies are engaged in an all-out, no-holds-barred struggle for dominance. (1.4)

12. A tiny metal shaving is responsible for the problem. (1.4)

13. She came to the office with a bruised, swollen knee. (1.4)

14. A chipped, cracked sheet of glass is useless to us. (1.4)

15. You'll receive our usual cheerful, prompt service. (1.4)

1.5: Adverbs

Practice Session

1.	least	6.	well-written	11.	well
2.	better	7.	well written	12.	really
3.	worse	8.	beautifully written	13.	slowly
4.	more competent	9.	credit card	14.	could hardly
5.	unique	10.	well	15.	more heavily

Level 1: Self-Assessment: Adjectives and Adverbs

1. good (1.5)

2. surely (1.5)

3. sick (1.5)

4. well (1.5)

5. good (1.5)

6. faster (1.5.2)

7. most recently (1.5.2)

8. more happily (1.5.2)

9. better (1.5.2)

10. most logically (1.5.2)

11. He doesn't seem to have any. *OR* He seems to have none. (1.5.1)

12. That machine is scarcely ever used. *OR* That machine is never used. (1.5.1)

13. They can't get any replacement parts until Thursday. *OR* They can get no replacement parts until Thursday. (1.5.1)

14. It wasn't any different from the first event we promoted. *OR* It was no different from the first event we promoted. (1.5.1)

15. We've looked for it, and it doesn't seem to be anywhere. *OR* We've looked for it, and it seems to be nowhere. (1.5.1)

1.6.1–1.6.3: Prepositions, Conjunctions, and Articles

Practice Session

1.	a	6.	a	11.	b
2.	b	7.	b	12.	b
3.	a	8.	a	13.	a
4.	b	9.	b	14.	a
5.	b	10.	a	15.	a

Level 1: Self-Assessment: Prepositions and Conjunctions

1. Where was your argument leading ~~to~~? (1.6.1)

2. I wish he would get off ~~of~~ the phone. (1.6.1)

3. This is a project ~~into which~~ you can sink your teeth <u>into</u> (1.6.1).

4. BMO Merchantile must become aware <u>of</u> and sensitive to its customers' concerns. (1.6.1)

5. We are responsible for aircraft safety in the air, <u>in</u> the hangars, and <u>on</u> the runways. (1.6.1)

6. to (1.6.1)

7.   among (1.6.1)

8.   for (1.6.1)

9.   to (1.6.1)

10.   from (1.6.1)

11.   She is active ~~in~~ not only <u>in</u> a civic group but also in an athletic organization. *OR* She is active in not only a civic group but also ~~in~~ an athletic organization. (1.6.2)

12.   That is either a mistake or ~~was~~ an intentional omission. (1.6.2)

13.   The question is whether to set up a booth at the convention or ~~be~~ <u>to</u> host a hospitality suite. (1.6.2)

14.   We are doing better ~~in~~ both <u>in</u> overall sales and in profits. *OR* in both overall sales and ~~in~~ profits. (1.6.2)

15.   She had neither the preferred educational background, nor ~~did she have~~ <u>the</u> suitable experience. (1.6.2)

1.7: Sentences

Practice Session

1.	a	4.	c	7.	c	10.	c
2.	b	5.	c	8.	c		
3.	b	6.	b	9.	a		

2.0: Punctuation

2.1–2.3: Periods, Question Marks, and Exclamation Points

Practice Session: Punctuation 1

1.	b	4.	b	7.	a	10.	c
2.	a *or* b	5.	a	8.	b		
3.	b	6.	b	9.	b		

170

Level 1: Self-Assessment—Periods, Question Marks, and Exclamation Points

1.   Dr. Eleanor H. Hutton has requested information on TaskMasters, Inc. (2.1)

2.   That qualifies us as a rapidly growing new company, don't you think? (2.2)

3.   Our president, Daniel Gruber, is a CGA. On your behalf, I asked him why he started the company. (2.1)

4.   In the past three years, we have experienced phenomenal growth of 800 percent. *OR* ! (2.3)

5.   Contact me at 1358 N. Bluff Avenue, Lethbridge, AB T1K 1L6. (2.1)

6.   Jack asked, "Why does he want to know? Maybe he plans to become a competitor." *OR* ! (2.2, 2.1, 2.3)

7.   The debt load fluctuates with the movement of the Bank of Canada prime rate. (2.1)

8.   I can't believe we could have missed such a promising opportunity! *OR* . (2.1, 2.2, 2.3)

9.   Is consumer loyalty extinct? Yes and no. (2.2, 2.1)

10.   Johnson and Kane, Inc., has gone out of business. What a surprise. *OR* ! (2.1, 2.3)

11.   Will you please send us a cheque today so that we can settle your account. *or* ? (2.2)

12.   Mr. James R. Capp will be our new CEO, beginning January 20, 2010. (2.1)

13.   The rag doll originally sold for $998, but we have lowered the price to a mere $599. (2.1)

14.   Will you be able to make the presentation at the conference, or should we find someone else? (2.2)

15.   So I ask you, "When will we admit defeat?" Never! (2.2, 2.3)

2.4–2.6: Semicolons, Colons, and Commas

Level 1: Self-Assessment—Semicolons, Colons, and Commas

1.   This letter looks good; that one doesn't. (2.4)

2.   I want to make one thing perfectly clear: neither of you will be promoted if sales figures don't improve. (2.5)

3.   The Zurich airport has been snowed in; therefore, I won't be able to meet with you before January 4. (2.4, 2.6)

4. His motivation was obvious: to get Meg fired. (2.5)

5. Only two firms have responded to our survey: J. J. Perkins and Tucker & Tucker. (2.5)

6. Send a copy to Mary Kwan, Marketing Director; Robert Bache, Comptroller; and Dennis Mann, Sales Director. (2.4)

7. Please be sure to interview these employees next week: Henry Gold, Doris Hatch, and George Iosupovich. (2.5, 2.6)

8. We have observed your hard work; because of it, we are promoting you to manager of your department. (2.4)

9. You shipped three items on June 7; however, we received only one of them. (2.4)

10. The convention kit includes the following: response cards, giveaways, brochures, and a display rack. (2.5)

11. The workers wanted an immediate wage increase; they had not had a raise in nearly two years. (2.4)

12. This, then, is our goal for 2011: to increase sales 35 percent. (2.5)

13. His writing skills are excellent; however, he still needs to polish his management style. (2.4, 2.6)

14. We would like to address three issues: efficiency, profitability, and market penetration. (2.5, 2.6)

15. Remember this rule: When in doubt, leave it out. (2.5)

Level 1: Self-Assessment—Commas

1. Please send us four cases of filters, two cases of wing nuts, and a bale of rags. (2.6)

2. Your analysis, however, does not account for returns. (2.6)

3. As a matter of fact, she has seen the figures. (2.6)

4. Before May 7, 2008, they wouldn't have minded either. (2.6)

5. After Martha has gone, talk to me about promoting her. (2.6)

6. Stoneridge, Inc., will go public on September 9, 2012. (2.6)

7. We want the new copier, not the old model. (2.6)

8. "Talk to me," Sandra said, "before you change a thing." (2.6)

9. Because of a previous engagement, Dr. Stoeve will not be able to attend. (2.6)

10. The company started attracting attention during the long, hard recession of the mid-1970s. (2.6)

11. You can reach me at this address: 717 Darby Place, Summerside, PE C1N 3TY. (2.6)

12. Transfer the documents from Sherbrooke, Quebec, to Don Mills, Ontario. (2.6)

13. Sam O'Neill, the designated representative, is gone today. (2.6)

14. With your help, we will soon begin. (2.6)

15. She may hire two new representatives, or she may postpone filling those territories until spring. (2.6)

2.6–2.13: Commas, Dashes, Hyphens, Quotation Marks, Parentheses, Ellipses, Underscores, and Italics

Practice Session: Punctuation 2

1.	b		6.	b		11.	b
2.	a		7.	b		12.	c
3.	a		8.	a		13.	a
4.	b		9.	b		14.	b
5.	a		10.	a		15.	b

Level 1: Self-Assessment—Dashes and Hyphens

1. Three qualities—speed, accuracy, and reliability—are desirable in any applicant to the data entry department. (2.7)

2. A highly placed source explained the top-secret negotiations. (2.8)

3. The file on Maria Wilson—yes, we finally found it—reveals a history of late payments. (2.7)

4. They're selling a well-designed machine. (2.8)

5. A bottle-green sports jacket is hard to find. (2.8)

6. Argentina, Brazil, Mexico—these are the countries we hope to concentrate on. (2.7)

7. Only two sites—maybe three—offer the things we need. (2.7)

8. How many owner-operators are in the industry? (2.8)

9. Your ever-faithful assistant deserves—without a doubt, I'm sure—a substantial raise. (2.8, 2.7)

10. Myrna Talefiero is this organization's president-elect. (2.8)

11. Stealth, secrecy, and surprise—those are the elements that will give us a competitive edge. (2.7)

12. The charts have been well placed on each page—unlike the running heads and footers. (2.8, 2.7)

13. We got our small-business loan—an enormous advantage. (2.8, 2.7)

14. Ron Franklin—do you remember him?—will be in town Monday. (2.7)

15. Your devil-may-care attitude affects everyone involved in the decision-making process (2.8)

Level 1: Self-Assessment—Quotation Marks, Parentheses, Ellipses, Underscores, and Italics

1. Be sure to read "How to Sell by Listening" in this month's issue of B.C. Business. (2.10, 2.13)

2. Her response (see the attached memo) is disturbing. (2.11)

3. Contact is an overused word. (2.13)

4. We will operate with a skeleton staff during the holiday break (December 21 through January 2). (2.11)

5. "The SBP's next conference," the bulletin noted, "will be held in Winnipeg." (2.10)

6. Sara O'Rourke (the Edmonton Sun reporter who will be interviewing us) will be here on Thursday. (2.11, 2.13)

7. I don't care why you didn't fill my order; I want to know when you'll fill it. (2.13)

8. The term up in the air means "undecided." (2.13, 2.10)

174

9. Her assistant (the one who just had the baby) won't be back for four weeks. (2.11)

10. As soon as the journalist heard Prime Minister Trudeau begin a sentence with "The state has no business in the bedrooms . . ." her jaw dropped. (2.10, 2.12)

11. Whom do you think <u>Time</u> magazine will select as its Person of the Year? (2.13)

12. Do you remember who sang <u>"Fall to Pieces"</u>? (2.10)

13. Refinements in robotics may prove profitable. (More detail about this technology appears in Appendix A.) (2.11)

14. The resignation letter begins, "Since I'll never regain your respect . . ." and goes on to explain why that's true. (2.10, 2.12)

15. You must help her distinguish between <u>i.e.</u> (which means "that is") and <u>e.g.</u> (which means "for example"). (2.12, 2.10)

3.0 Mechanics

Practice Session

1.	c	4.	a	7.	b	10.	a
2.	b	5.	a	8.	b		
3.	b	6.	c	9.	a		

3.1–3.2: Capitals and Abbreviations

Level 1: Self-Assessment—Capitals and Abbreviations

1. Dr. <u>Paul Singha</u> is joining our staff. (3.1)

2. New <u>C</u>aressa skin cream should be in a position to dominate that market. (3.1)

3. Send this report to ~~mister~~ Mr. H. K. Danforth, <u>P.O.</u> Box 2243 <u>R</u>iley, <u>AB</u> TJ5 4S2. (3.1, 3.2)

4. You are responsible for training my new assistant to operate the <u>X</u>erox machine. (3.1)

5. She received her <u>MBA</u> from the <u>U</u>niversity of New Brunswick. (3.1, 3.2)

6. The building is located on Champlain <u>S</u>treet near Alcan <u>P</u>lace. (3.1)

7. Call me early in the a.m. morning, and I'll have the information you need. (3.2)

8. When Jones becomes <u>CEO</u> next month, we'll need your input. (3.2)

9. Address it to <u>H</u>ead of <u>P</u>roduction <u>A</u>rt <u>B</u>owers. (3.1)

10. Please <u>RSVP</u> to <u>S</u>ony corp. Corporation just as soon as you know your schedule. (3.1, 3.2)

11. The data-processing department will begin work on feb. February 2, just one wk. week from today. (3.1, 3.2)

12. You are to meet her on <u>F</u>riday in her office at the <u>E</u>conomics dept. Department. (3.1, 3.2)

13. Whenever you can come, <u>P</u>rofessor, our employees will greatly enjoy your presentation. (3.1)

14. At 50 per box, our std. standard contract forms are $9.00 a box, and our warranty forms are $7.95 a box. (3.2)

15. We plan to establish a sales office on the <u>W</u>est <u>C</u>oast. (3.1)

3.3: Numbers

Level 1: Self-Assessment—Numbers

1. We need to hire ~~one~~ 1 office manager, ~~four~~ 4 bookkeepers, and ~~twelve~~ 12 assistants. (3.3)

2. The market for this product is nearly ~~six~~ 6 million people in our region alone. (3.3)

3. Make sure that all 1835 pages are on my desk no later than ~~nine o'clock~~ 9:00 a.m. (or *nine o'clock in the morning*) (3.3)

4. In 2008, ~~was the year that~~ Jasminder Bohal sold more than $50 000 ~~thousand dollars~~ worth of stock. (3.3)

5. Our deadline is ~~2010/09/22~~ September 22, 2010, but we won't be ready before ~~2011/02/22~~ February 22, 2011. (or *22 September 2010 ... 22 February 2011*) (3.3)

6. ~~95~~ Ninety-five percent of our customers are men. *OR* Of our customers, 95 percent are men. (3.3)

7. More than ~~1/2~~ half the Canadian population is female. (3.3)

8. Cecile Simmons, ~~thirty-eight~~ 38, is the first woman in this company to be promoted to management. (3.3)

176

9. Last year, I wrote 20 ~~15~~-fifteen-page reports, and Michelle wrote 24 three-page reports. (3.3)

10. Of the 15 applicants, ~~seven~~ 7 are qualified. (3.3)

11. Our blinds should measure 90 cm wide by ~~one and one-half metres~~ 1.5 m long by 4 cm deep. (3.3)

12. Deliver the couch to ~~seven eighty-three~~ 783 Fountain Rd., Suite ~~three~~ 3, Drayton Valley, AB T4N 5H5. (3.3)

13. Here are the corrected figures: 42.7<u>0</u>% agree, 23.25% disagree, 34.<u>00</u>% are undecided, and the error is <u>0</u>.05%. (3.3)

14. You have to agree that 5 ~~000 000~~ million Canadian citizens cannot be wrong. (3.3)

15. We need a set of shelves ~~1 point two five metres~~ 1.25 m long. (3.3)

4.0: Vocabulary

4.1: Frequently Confused Words

Practice Session

1. accepted
2. advice
3. affect
4. borne
5. capital
6. cite
7. complement
8. counsel
9. discreet
10. lien
11. loath
12. ordinances
13. peddle
14. prosecute
15. precedents
16. principal
17. role
18. sheer
19. stationery
20. whether

4.2: Frequently Misused Words

Practice Session

1. a lot
2. to
3. uninterested
4. implying
5. inferred

6. fewer
7. as if
8. regardless
9. to
10. an oral

4.3: Frequently Misspelled Words

Practice Session

1. accommodate
2. clientele
3. changeable
4. consensus
5. embarrassing
6. existence
7. harassment
8. independent

9. leisure
10. necessary
11. occurring
12. preferred
13. received
14. separate
15. vicious

Level 1: Self-Assessment—Vocabulary

1. except (4.1)
2. device (4.1)
3. loath (4.1)
4. ordinance (4.1)
5. precedence (4.1)

6.   than (4.1)

7.   who's (4.1)

8. a lot In this department, we see <u>alot</u> of mistakes like that. (4.2)

9. eligible Three more <u>elegible</u> candidates are waiting to be interviewed. (4.3)

10. regardless He decided to reveal the information, <u>irregardless</u> of the consequences. (4.2)

11. accommodate Why not go along when it is so easy to <u>accomodate</u> his demands? (4.3)

12. imply When you say that, do you mean to <u>infer</u> that I'm being unfair? (4.2)

13. embarrassing She says that she finds this sort of ceremony <u>embarassing</u>. (4.3)

14. to All we have to do is try <u>and</u> get along with him for a few more days. (4.2)

15. precede A friendly handshake should always <u>preceed</u> negotiations. (4.3)

Correction Symbols

Instructors often use these short, easy-to-remember correction symbols and abbreviations when evaluating students' writing. You can use them too, to understand your instructor's suggestions and to revise and proofread your own letters, memos, and reports.

CONTENT AND STYLE

Acc	Accuracy. Check to be sure information is correct.
ACE	Avoid copying examples.
ACP	Avoid copying problems.
Adp	Adapt. Tailor message to reader.
App	Approach. Follow proper organizational approach—either direct order (the main idea comes first, followed by the evidence) or indirect order (the evidence comes first, and the main idea comes later).
Assign	Assignment. Review instructions for assignment.
AV	Active verb. Substitute active for passive.
Awk	Awkward phrasing. Rewrite.
BC	Be consistent.
BMS	Be more sincere.
Chop	Choppy sentences. Use longer sentences and more transitional phrases.
Con	Condense. Use fewer words.
CT	Conversational tone. Avoid using overly formal language.
Depers	Depersonalize. Avoid attributing credit or blame to any individual or group.
Dev	Develop. Provide greater detail.
Dir	Direct. Use direct approach; get to the point.
Emph	Emphasize. Develop this point more fully.
EW	Explanation weak. Check logic; provide more proof.
Fl	Flattery. Avoid compliments that are insincere.

180

FS	Figure of speech. Find a more accurate expression.
GNF	Good news first. Use direct order.
GRF	Give reasons first. Use indirect order.
GW	Goodwill. Put more emphasis on expressions of goodwill.
H/E	Honesty/ethics. Revise statement to reflect good business practices.
Imp	Imply. Avoid being direct.
Inc	Incomplete. Develop further.
Jar	Jargon. Use less specialized language.
Log	Logic. Check development of argument.
Neg	Negative. Use more positive approach or expression.
Obv	Obvious. Do not state point in such detail.
OC	Overconfident. Adopt humbler language.
OM	Omission.
Org	Organization. Strengthen outline.
OS	Off the subject. Close with point on main subject.
Par	Parallel. Use same structure.
Pom	Pompous. Rephrase in down-to-earth terms.
PV	Point of view. Make statement from reader's perspective rather than your own.
RB	Reader benefit. Explain what reader stands to gain.
Red	Redundant. Reduce number of times this point is made.
Ref	Reference. Cite source of information.
Rep	Repetitive. Provide different expression.
RS	Resale. Reassure reader that he or she has made a good choice.
SA	Service attitude. Put more emphasis on helping reader.
Sin	Sincerity. Avoid sounding glib or uncaring.

SL	Stereotyped language. Focus on individual's characteristics instead of on false generalizations.
Spec	Specific. Provide more specific statement.
SPM	Sales promotion material. Tell reader about related goods or services.
Stet	Let stand (let the words remain in their original form).
Sub	Subordinate. Make this point less important.
SX	Sexist. Avoid language that contributes to gender stereotypes.
Tone	Tone needs improvement.
Trans	Transition. Show connection between points.
UAE	Use action ending. Close by stating what reader should do next.
UAS	Use appropriate salutation.
UAV	Use active voice.
Unc	Unclear. Rewrite to clarify meaning.
UPV	Use passive voice.
USS	Use shorter sentences.
V	Variety. Use different expression or sentence pattern.
W	Wordy. Eliminate unnecessary words.
WC	Word choice. Find a more appropriate word.
YA	"You" attitude. Rewrite to emphasize reader's needs.

182

GRAMMAR, MECHANICS, AND USAGE

Ab	Abbreviation. Avoid abbreviations in most cases; use correct abbreviation.
Adj	Adjective. Use adjective instead.
Adv	Adverb. Use adverb instead.
Agr	Agreement. Make subject and verb or noun and pronoun agree.
Ap	Appearance. Improve appearance.
Apos	Apostrophe. Check use of apostrophe.
Art	Article. Use correct article.
BC	Be consistent.
Cap	Capitalize.
Case	Use cases correctly.
CoAdj	Coordinate adjective. Insert comma between coordinate adjectives; delete comma between adjective and compound noun.
CS	Comma splice. Use period or semicolon to separate clauses.
DM	Dangling modifier. Rewrite so that modifier clearly relates to subject of sentence.
Exp	Expletive. Avoid expletive beginnings, such as *it is*, *there are*, *there is*, *this is*, and *these are*.
F	Format. Improve layout of document.
Frag	Fragment. Rewrite as complete sentence.
Gram	Grammar. Correct grammatical error.
HCA	Hyphenate compound adjective.
lc	Lower case. Do not use capital letter.
M	Margins. Improve frame around document.
MM	Misplaced modifier. Place modifier close to word it modifies.
NRC	Nonrestrictive clause (or phrase). Separate from rest of sentence with commas.
P	Punctuation. Use correct punctuation.

Par	Parallel. Use same structure.
PH	Place higher. Move document up on page.
PL	Place lower. Move document down on page.
Prep	Preposition. Use correct preposition.
RC	Restrictive clause (or phrase). Remove commas that separate clause from rest of sentence.
RO	Run-on sentence. Separate two sentences with comma and coordinating conjunction or with semicolon.
SC	Series (serial) comma. Add comma before *and*.
SI	Split infinitive. Do not separate *to* from rest of verb.
Sp	Spelling error. Consult dictionary.
S-V	Subject-verb pair. Do not separate with comma.
Syl	Syllabification. Divide word between syllables.
WD	Word division. Check dictionary for proper end-of-line hyphenation.
WW	Wrong word. Replace with another word.

Proofreading Marks

Symbol	Meaning	Symbol Used in Context	Corrected Copy
═══╎╎	Align horizontally	meaningful result	meaningful result
‖	Align vertically	1. Power cable 2. Keyboard	1. Power cable 2. Keyboard
≡	Capitalize	Pepsico, Inc.	PepsiCo, Inc.
⊐⊏	Centre	⌐Awards Banquet⌐	Awards Banquet
⌣	Close up space	self- confidence	self-confidence
ℓ	Delete	harassment and abuse	harassment
(ds)	Double-space	text in first line text in second line (ds)	text in first line text in second line
∧	Insert	tirquoise shirts	turquoise and white shirts
∨̌	Insert apostrophe	our teams goals	our team's goals
∧̌	Insert comma	a, b and c	a, b, and c
≐∧	Insert hyphen	third quarter sales	third-quarter sales
⊙	Insert period	Harrigan et al	Harrigan et al.
∀̌ ∀̌	Insert quotation marks	This team isn't cooperating.	This "team" isn't cooperating.
♯	Insert space	real estate testcase	real estate test case
/	Lower case	TULSA, South of here	Tulsa, south of here
⌞⌟	Move down	Sincerely,	Sincerely,
⊏	Move left	Attention: ⌐ Security	Attention: Security
⊐	Move right	February 2, 2009 ⌐⌐	February 2, 2009
⌐⌐	Move up	THIRD-QUARTER SALES	THIRD-QUARTER SALES
(STET)	Restore	staff talked openly and frankly (STET)	staff talked openly
⌒	Run lines together	Manager, Distribution	Manager, Distribution
(ss)	Single space	text in first line text in second line	text in first line text in second line
⬭	Spell out	(COD)	cash on delivery
(sp)	Spell out	(sp) Assn. of Biochem. Engrs.	Association of Biochemical Engineers
⌐⌐	Start new line	Marla Fenton, Manager, Distribution	Marla Fenton, Manager, Distribution
¶	Start new paragraph	¶The solution is easy to determine but difficult to implement in a competitive environment like the one we now face.	The solution is easy to determine but difficult to implement in a competitive environment like the one we now face.
∼	Transpose	airy, light, casual tone	light, airy, casual tone
(bf)	Use boldface	Recommendations (bf)	**Recommendations**
(ital)	Use italics	Quarterly Report (ital)	*Quarterly Report*

NOTES

NOTES